How It Works
How to Fix It

OUTDOOR POWER EQUIPMENT

ARTHUR DARACK

STEIN AND DAY / *Publishers* / New York

Contents

First published in 1977   Copyright © 1977 by Arthur Darack
All rights reserved   Designed by Brenda Darack
Printed in the United States of America

STEIN AND DAY/ *Publishers* /Scarborough House,
Briarcliff Manor, N.Y. 10510

Credits: Illustrations from Briggs & Stratton; Gilson Brothers Co.; John Deere; Black & Decker; Ariens Co.; International Harvester; Clinton Engines Corp.; Tecumseh Products Co.; Disston; Electro Engineering Products Co., Inc.; Skil; Rockwell Power Tools; Gilson Brothers Co.; Toro Mfg. Co.; Stanley Power Tools.

Library of Congress Cataloging in Publication Data

Darack, Arthur.
    Outdoor power equipment.

    1. Power tools.   2. Gardening—Equipment and
supplies.   I. Title.
TJ1195.D35   635.9'1'37   77-7044
ISBN 0-8128-2344-3   ISBN 0-8128-2276-5 pbk.

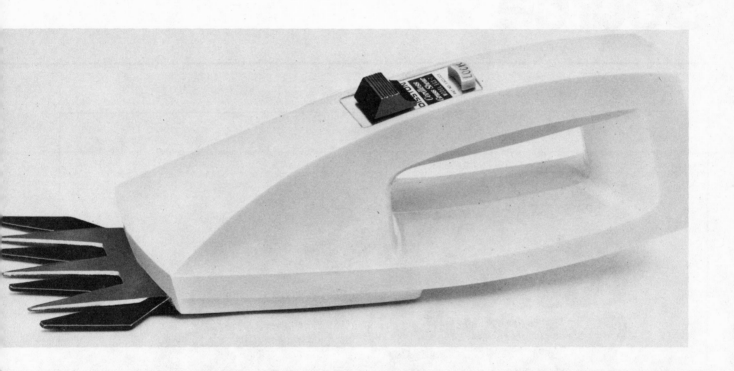

Chapter One

The Power Source

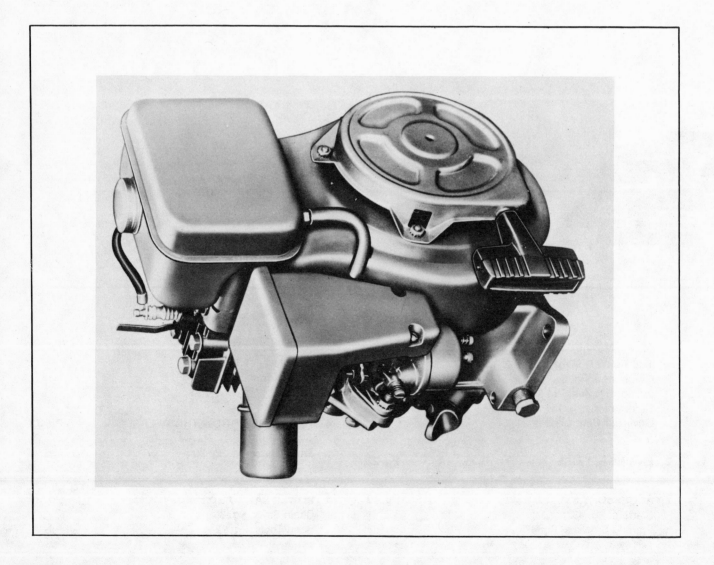

When your lawn mower gasoline engine sputters and balks, stalls and won't start, the problems are similar to those involving bigger engines. Your lawn mower engine is a one-cylinder version of your four, six, or eight cylinder auto engine. Because it has only one cylinder to keep it going, when that one falters the jig is up, whereas when one of your car cylinders weakens you can count on some performance, however lame, out of the rest of them.

Just as you can learn to keep your car engine in more or less good working order, if you are willing to invest the time in it, and the rather small number of dollars for tools and equipment, so you can do the same operation on your lawn mower engine, with small tool and equipment needs. Since lawn mower engine repair is fairly simple and increasingly costly it represents a good way to sneak via the back door into the home auto repair field, which is more complex and drastically more expensive. But, auto repair is not the reason for this book. Small engine and outdoor motorized tools and equipment are its subject, chief of them the power (gas engine) lawn mower. The market being what it is nowadays, that small engine is almost certainly going to be a Briggs & Stratton 3 or 3½ horsepower engine, because that manufacturer fairly well dominates the small engine field, accounting for over two-thirds of all lawn mower engines sold. The 3 or 3½ horsepower engine is the most common size, with its wind-up or rope starter. Self-propelled and riding lawn-mowers add horsepower and the extra systems and components the added capabilities demand. Riding mowers are small (dangerous) vehicles, with the instabilities of motorcycles and small cars. Self-propelled mowers are considerably less complex than the riding types, but do involve some kind of attachment, gearing and bearings, to make the thing move as well as cut grass.

Mower engines get out of whack more quickly than cars because they are more crude and unstable, and their vibrations, plus the beatings they take, change carburetor and ignition settings, while the dirt and dust generated by the blade takes its toll. Then too, an engine wears normally from use. And if you don't change its oil regularly the normal wear occurs at a quickened tempo. Finally, the mower takes hard knocks as it bumps and grinds into trees and rocks. One of the most common designs combines gas tank with carburetor. When the tank gets banged around too heartily, the carburetor seating is destroyed and the engine does crazy things, like speeding up for no apparent reason, slowing down, dying, and refusing to start.

Let us resolve to cure this problem, and understand all the other symptoms and cures in the life of a lawn mower engine, perilous as it can be. We will then come to grips with the peripheral systems outside the engine that drive the blade and the self-propelling mechanism. The riding mower systems that are distinct from the engine but connected to it, like your car engine, will follow. Riding mowers, like cars, need transmissions, some method of starting and stopping rather more advanced than the mower you push. We'll see about that.

The mower you push, which you can buy for any price from $50 (on sale) to $150 and more, will contain handle, wheels, deck, chute and bag, engine and controls. It may or may not contain an electric cranking device. If you take care of the engine and other moving parts, changing oil, adjusting the carburetor, points and plug periodically, and replacing all wearing parts as required, you can expect the engine to last quite a few years. The writer nursed a Briggs & Stratton small engine for 10 years, and it was still quite operable, excepting that the deck was rusted.

Wheels and their axles, decks, engine controls

and handles get rusty unless you keep after them. Blades need sharpening each season. A dull blade makes the engine work harder, shortening its life. Unless the points of deterioration are tackled once a season, you'll be buying a new mower every two or three years. You may decide that it's cheaper to do it that way, or you may not. Mowers are inexpensive enough to discard them after a couple of seasons of wear, rather than pay $25 or more to repair them. But increasingly we believe it is essential to repair the thing rather than discard it. Raw materials are not inexhaustible; the charge that the U.S. gorges itself on disposable materials it unfeelingly grabs from abroad gets a tiny confirmation each time we throw something out that we could repair and restore to duty.

Given the will, what tools do we need to maintain a lawn mower and other power tools? A small auto socket wrench set is not essential but marvelously helpful for the simplest maintenance. It is indispensable for engine tuneup and other more radical tinkering. Then, you need a tiny assortment of small tools — a hammer with lead or hard rubber head, a small vise or vise pliers, and some engine oil, penetrating oil to help loosen rusted nuts and bolts, and a small can of bearing grease. Spark plug tools required are a spark plug socket, a gapping tool and a file or piece of sandpaper to clean off the electrodes. Emery boards that some people use on fingernails are good. Then you may want a file for the mower blade — better yet, an attachment that fits a hand drill that will file the blade with precision. Of course, that requires a drill, that indispensable tool for every task you used to do by hand.

OIL CHANGE

Engine oil change is easy enough. Drain the old oil after it is warm. If you drain cold oil you've wasted your time because the engine-damaging sludge will be left behind, in the engine. To find the oil plug, look beneath the engine somewhere near the blade. Safety dictates that whenever you get involved with the blade you disconnect the spark plug cable — pull it off and tie it away from the plug so any turning of the blade won't start the engine. You may laugh derisively at the possibility when you have to crank the thing a half dozen times to get it started usually, but remember we're talking about a warm engine which normally will start quickly.

The oil plug is usually a square plug that must be

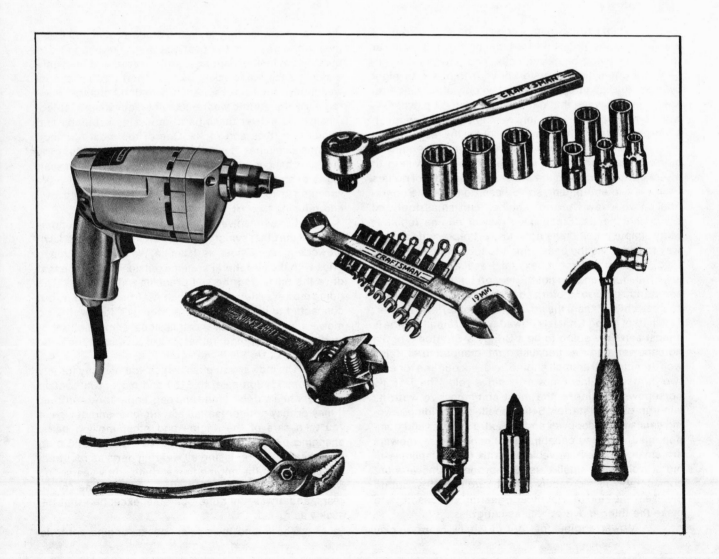

BASIC MODEL SERIES		CAPACITY
Aluminum		Pints
6, 8, 9 Cu. in. Vert. Crankshaft		1-1/4
6, 8, 9 Cu. in. Horiz. Crankshaft		1-1/4
10, 13 Cu. in. Vert. Crankshaft		1-3/4
10, 13 Cu. in. Horiz. Crankshaft		1-1/4
14, 17 Cu. in. Vert. Crankshaft		2-1/4
14, 17, 19 Cu. in. Horiz. Crankshaft		2-3/4
Cast Iron		
9, 14, 19, 20 Cu. in. Horiz. Crankshaft		3
23, 24, 30, 32 Cu. in. Horiz. Crankshaft		4

SUMMER
(Above 40° F.)
Use SAE 30

If not available,
Use SAE 10W-30
or
SAE 10W-40

WINTER
(Under 40° F.)
Use SAE 5W-20 or SAE 5W-30
If not available,
Use SAE 10W or SAE 10W-30
Below 0° F,
Use SAE 10W or SAE 10W-30
Diluted 10% with Kerosene

When you change engine oil you should also change oil in the sponge at the top of the carburetor. This sponge is the air filter. It catches grass and other things you don't want entering your carburetor. Also, while you change oil you can think about removing the blade and sharpening it, since the blade requires the same maneuver to expose it — propping up the mower at a suitable height — as the oil plug. To sharpen the blade requires a fitted stone and ¼-inch drill to drive it. You can buy the stone at any good hardware. Undoubtedly you have the ¼-inch drill. If not, buy a Skil, Black & Decker, Ward, or Sears, and you're in business. All these firms (and others) market the correct accessories for the drill.

Back to the sponge on top of the carburetor (in the air filter housing which is that oddly shaped container above the gas tank, though sometimes it's a circular thing on a separate carburetor near but not necessarily on top of the gas tank). A long screw or wing nut, will hold the housing top that conceals the sponge filter. Remove the screw-bolt or whatever, take off the top, and there will be

opened with an open-end wrench, though in a pinch you can find a socket to do the job. Or use an adjustable open end. To get the plug open may require propping the mower up on a box of some sort. You don't want to turn it upside down because that will spill gas and oil all over everything. So, get a pan to catch the old oil, prop up the mower sufficiently to give you a shot at the plug, loosen it, then turn it out by hand and let the oil drain out completely. Replace the plug when the oil stops dripping. Put the mower back on the ground, and open the oil filler cap. It's usually a plastic cap, located alongside the engine at one side of the deck, that you might be able to turn off by hand. If not, use a screwdriver as a lever to start the cap out. Refill with oil almost to the top, then replace the cap.

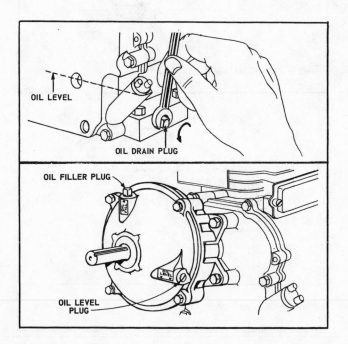

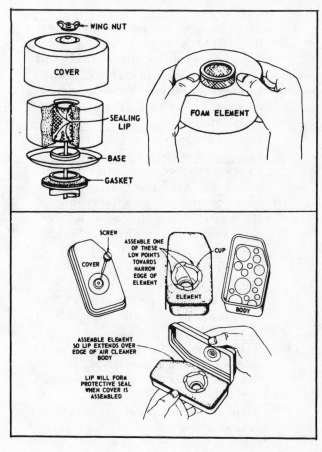

the filter, snugly secured but removable. Wash it in kerosene or liquid detergent and water, squeeze it dry and wrap it in a cloth to complete drying. Saturate the sponge now with engine oil, squeeze out the excess oil and replace.

Large Briggs & Stratton engines have dry air

cleaners, like automobiles. Other small engine manufacturers also use the dry element cleaner. It can be made of metal or paper. If metal, wash in kerosene, gasoline, detergent; if paper, merely tap it on the ground until you can see the dirt coming away, or use a vacuum cleaner attachment on it, or buy a new one. One antiquated form of cleaner, that used to be fairly common, is the oil bath. This is a metal element seated in a housing containing oil. The oil should be replaced when it is dirty, the element cleaned out. Be careful; oil is messy.

TUNEUP PROCEDURE

1. Remove air cleaner, check for proper servicing.
2. Check oil level and drain. (Clean fuel tank and lines if separate from carburetor).
3. Remove blower housing, inspect rope and rewind assembly and starter clutch.
4. Clean cooling fins and entire engine. Rock flywheel to check compression.
5. Remove carburetor, disassemble and inspect for wear or damage. Wash in solvent, replace parts as necessary and assemble. Set initial adjustment.
6. Inspect crossover tube or intake elbow for damaged gaskets.
7. Check governor blade, linkage and spring for damage or wear, if mechanical also check adjustment.
8. Remove flywheel, check for seal leakage, both flywheel and PTO sides. Check flywheel key.
9. Remove breaker cover and check for proper sealing.
10. Inspect breaker points and condenser. Replace or clean and adjust. Check plunger.
11. Check coil, inspect all wires for breaks, damaged insulation. Be sure lead wires do not touch flywheel. Check stop switch and lead.
12. Replace breaker cover, use sealer where wires enter.
13. Install flywheel, time engine if necessary. Set air gap. Check for spark.
14. Remove cylinder head, check gasket, remove spark plug, and clean carbon, inspect valves for seating.
15. Replace cylinder head, torque to specified torque, set spark plug gap or replace plug if necessary.
16. Replace oil and fuel, check muffler for restrictions or damage.
17. Adjust remote control linkage and cable if used, for correct operation.
18. Service air cleaner, check gaskets and element for damage.
19. Run and adjust mixture and top speed.

IGNITION SERVICE

The two most common breakdowns in a mower engine are electrical and fuel. The mower won't start. First, pull gently on the spark plug cable to remove it from the plug. Now hold the cable tip 1/8th-inch from any point on the engine, and turn the flywheel, either by hand or by the use of the starter or windup mechanism. A spark should jump vividly across the gap with a snap. If it does, this means that the trouble is possibly in the spark plug, but probably in the fuel system. It is best to buy a new plug, when the engine doesn't start. That saves a lot of work if the trouble actually is in the plug. But let's assume that when you get a spark in the test we've just done that the problem is in the fuel system. Remove the air cleaner as before and look into the throat of the carburetor, where

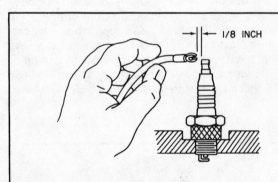

This tests electrical production.

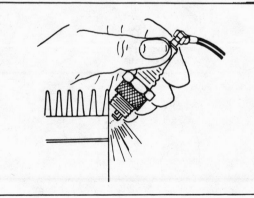

This tests spark plug efficiency.

you will see a circular valve (choke) large enough to block the entire throat when closed. If, when you go through the starting procedure you see gasoline in evidence in the carburetor, you can be fairly sure that the choke has gotten out of whack. The fault may also be in the air vane governor, a flapping, metal flag that opens the throttle under some circumstances. The air vane is manipulated by a link spring that attaches to the throttle control on the handle.

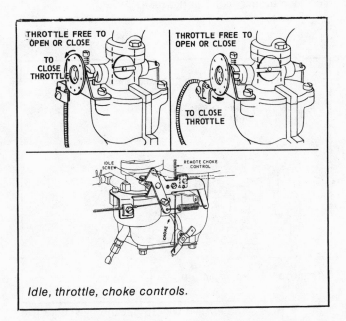

Idle, throttle, choke controls.

The air vane is next to the flywheel, that finned, under-the-screen wheel that spins around at high speed or low, and is at the top of the engine, just below the windup or rope starter mechanism. You can see the air vane by peeking between the flywheel and the magneto coil, which looks like any transformer. To check out the air vane, go through the regular starting procedure and move the air vane control slightly forward and backward, noting what effect, if any, the movement has. If the engine catches suddenly at a certain point of movement, note precisely where it happens so that it can be set at that point. Of course, the usual carburetor adjustment on balky engines or engines hard to start is the fuel-air mixture screw that controls the ratio of air to gas. This screw, on the front plate facing you as you push the mower, is subject to engine vibration and wear. Turn it all the way in, gently, until it bottoms. Don't turn it past the first, feathery touch. Carburetors are delicate creatures. Once it touches, then turn it back out, two complete turns. Now try. This adjustment, and the air vane manipulation, should clue you into the fuel situation. If playing with the air-gas mixture makes the engine run properly the problem is simplicity itself. It is unlikely that the air vane by itself can alter the picture completely, or as completely as the air-gas mixture adjustment. But both adjustments will often get the engine started, assuming that ignition is working.

At the moment we are assuming that it is not,

purely for reasons of explanation. The fact is that both ignition and fuel systems deteriorate simultaneously — after all, they are both working at the same time and it follows that they will demand equal rest at the same time. And since they are interdependent, it is hard in practice to separate them. Hence tests often must be made on both of them. You have only two hands and the nature of the beast is such that you can't really test the two systems exactly simultaneously. So, you test them, and work on them more or less in parallel. So, back to ignition.

It was suggested that you buy a new spark plug each time trouble arises. That's overkill. You might start by removing the old one, cleaning and gapping it. At least, you might do that first. It takes only a few minutes. To clean the plug requires its removal. This takes the spark plug socket and a bar or wrench to turn the socket once it is fitted over the plug. A spark plug socket usually has a rubber interior jacket to prevent the porcelain from being damaged during removal or installation. This is your cue; when turning it in or out, don't push the socket wrench to one side, but keep it exactly centered as you turn. This will save the porcelain. Cracked porcelain requires replacing the plug.

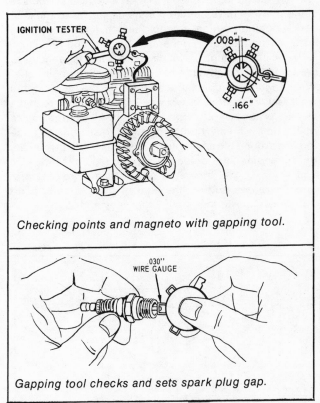

Checking points and magneto with gapping tool.

Gapping tool checks and sets spark plug gap.

Once the plug is removed, inspect the electrode surfaces. Clean them off with sandpaper or a small file, then check the gap with a gapping tool. (It costs about $1.) The gap should be .030 on Briggs & Stratton engines, .025 for Clinton, and the same for the one other engine you may encounter, the Kohler. Clean all the carbon and other material off the spark plug electrodes and surfaces, sand them off and set the gap if it isn't right. The gap is the distance between the curved electrode that goes from the circular rim of the plug over to the fixed center electrode that peeks out of its cylindrical casing inside the plug. Don't ever push the center electrode around for any reason; the outside, curving, electrode is the one you adjust. You adjust it with the gapping tool which has a U cutout that will fit the electrode snugly for bending in or out. Set the electrode so the feeler gauge will fit closely between it and the center pole.

Check the spark plug cable and clean off the tip that fits over the plug. Make sure the cable's insulation hasn't been worn away by the engine shroud (cover). If it has, get a new cable or (better yet) wrap a couple of layers of heavy tape around it, as long as there's nothing wrong with the wire.

Spark plugs, if cleaned and gapped, should last several seasons. There are two sizes of plugs, ¾-inch and 13/16-inch socket size, with the latter predominating. For Briggs & Stratton engines you can use Champion CJ-8 or J-8; Auto-Lite A-7NX or A-71, or A.C. CS-45 or GC-56. When replacing your plug buy the original number. When you tighten the plug at installation, bring it up snugly, but not as if you're saving the republic. Too tight is worse than not tight enough. The next operation should be points and condenser, finally the magneto.

It should be noted here that electrical systems in some mowers have cranking systems similar to those in cars — ignition switch, solenoid switch, ignition warning light, starting motor — generator, battery, and regulator. All these components have their pitfalls and tendencies to break down, exactly as with cranking systems in cars. We'll continue with smaller engines for the moment, but we'll tackle the starting systems later. While we are in the vicinity of the spark plug it might be well to urge you to police up the area, by brushing away grass from the cooling fins around the spark plug. Grass anywhere in quantity on the engine interferes with cooling (so does dirty oil), and anything that increases engine operating temperature decreases engine life (true of people, cars, hand drills, lawn mowers and any other moving tool).

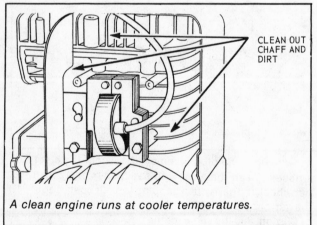

CLEAN OUT CHAFF AND DIRT

A clean engine runs at cooler temperatures.

The next stop on the ignition circuit is to get at the points and condenser. That requires removal of the flywheel screen, starter clutch, the flywheel itself, and the aluminum housing that covers points and condenser. In order to get at these components you must first remove the rope or windup starter, as the case may be. This requires that first you unbolt the engine cover (below the plastic shroud on some models) that contains the starter mechanism, as well as anything attached to the engine shroud — the handlebar controls, for example. Two bolts in the rear of the cover, two in front, and a stray screw or two elsewhere will get the engine cover off and expose the flywheel screen. This has four small screws that come out with either screwdriver or small socket wrench, bringing you face to face with the flywheel.

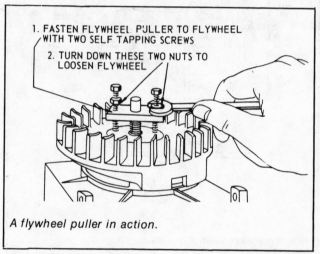

1. FASTEN FLYWHEEL PULLER TO FLYWHEEL WITH TWO SELF TAPPING SCREWS

2. TURN DOWN THESE TWO NUTS TO LOOSEN FLYWHEEL

A flywheel puller in action.

Here's the easiest way to get the flywheel off a typical Briggs & Stratton engine. Once the screen is off the top, the next part to be removed is the starter clutch housing (on windup starters — the kind with a metal crank that folds over). To get the starter clutch off take a block of wood, say about three or four inches long and from a piece of 2X4. Put it against each of the three notches at the base of the clutch in turn, and hit the wood block sharply (counter-clockwise) until the clutch turns. Unscrew it and now you face the flywheel itself, held in place by friction and a slotted key. The easy way to remove the flywheel is with a special puller. It's inexpensive and advisable, but you don't need it. With a soft head hammer — either lead or hard rubber — hit the top of the crankshaft, which is that metal protuberance you have exposed, as you pull up on the flywheel from below with your spare hand. Pull up sufficiently to lift the mower slightly off the ground, then bang the crankshaft solidly with the soft hammer. Don't use a steel hammer; you risk ruining the crankshaft and bearings. Of course, that flywheel puller, for a few dollars, is the approved method if your fastidiousness gets in the way of the crude, hammer-blow method above.

Another small Briggs & Stratton engine type with a rope starter (and some of them with an electric starter) have yet another method of holding on to the flywheel. This type has a ½-inch nut that you turn to the right to loosen — that's the opposite of the usual counter-clockwise spin for unscrewing nuts and bolts. This type is good because it offers a neat opportunity to get the flywheel off. You put a couple of "shock" nuts on the crankshaft end — any two nuts that fit — and pound on them, pulling up on the flywheel with your free hand, making sure that you don't hit the end of the crankshaft, which you can't so long as you don't screw the nuts down below the top of the crankshaft.

Turn the crankshaft and watch the points. Do they open slightly and close tightly? That's what you'll be aiming at with the new set. Now check out the point surfaces. If they are smooth and un-pitted, there is no point in replacing them. But if the points haven't been changed in a year or two, and you've gone to all this trouble so far, be a big spender and put in a new set, cost about $3 or $4, depending on what all the kit contains.

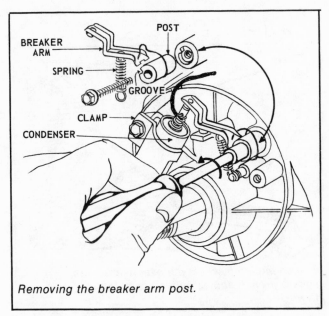

Removing the breaker arm post.

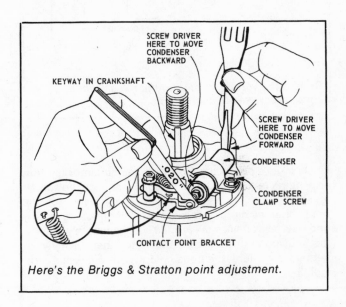

Here's the Briggs & Stratton point adjustment.

When the flywheel comes off, remove the key — that little metal finger that seems lost on the side of either the flywheel or the housing — and don't misplace it. Now you are face to face with the aluminum housing for the points and condenser. It is held with a couple of small screws. Remove them (small socket wrench), and pry off the aluminum housing. It will be stuck in gummy stuff. Notice the wires emerging from the housing. Inspect them to make sure that insulation hasn't worn off. The cover is fitted tightly in order to keep out dust that might foul the points. The tight fit won't keep oil out if the engine sends it through a worn point plunger. A thin show of oil isn't too important, but an emphatic coating means a major job.

Point gap must be adjusted precisely to .020 inch.

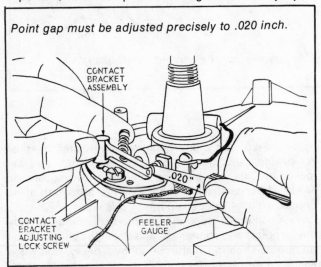

Assuming there is no oil problem, let's take out the old point-condenser set — in small engines they're combined — and install the new. Notice that the cylindrical condenser is held by a clamp that unscrews, and the moving point is held in place by a small spring that keeps the end of the moving point arm locked into a groove in a stubby post that also is unscrewed for removal purposes. It's easy enough to get all this apart, but what isn't so easy is to get the wire back into the condenser top if you lose the little plastic tool that comes with the points and serves only that one function. Okay, that wire comes out of the old condenser easily enough if you just lean on it a bit. But then, to get the wire back into the new condenser requires the plastic cap. It fits over the point and you push it in sufficiently to expose the hole that accepts the wire. Once this is done, and the condenser is seated in its clamp, the movable point screwed in and settled into its slot, now whip out the feeler gauge and set the gap at .020. You do this, obviously, by pushing the condenser closer in to the moving point or back away from it, then tightening the clamp. When tightened, check the gap again. It can change during the tightening process.

Retrace the steps you took to dismantle the engine thus far. Put the aluminum housing back, making sure that the cable going out of it is in the exact groove that it fits. Tighten the two screws carefully so as not to distort the housing — firmly but not actually very tight. Then replace the flywheel and its key, taking care that the

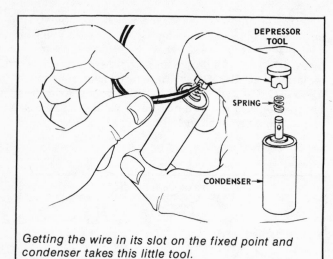

Getting the wire in its slot on the fixed point and condenser takes this little tool.

off, the key and slot are exposed, and both flywheel and crankshaft are tapered to fit each other snugly. This tapered fit is important, along with the key. If the fitted surfaces have bright marks on them, instead of dull, uniform surfaces it's a sign of incorrect fitting. Correct fit is easily obtained if you take two precautions — fit the key precisely and tighten the nut atop the crankshaft snugly and to correct torque.

key is in its slot, snugly. Screw on the clutch or the nut, depending on the model, fairly tightly, replace the screen and fit the starter housing and engine cover back. You will notice that the clutch fits into the starter housing in only one way, so don't fumble around with it aimlessly; look at the housing and the clutch and match them visually together, then plunk the housing down on crankshaft and clutch.

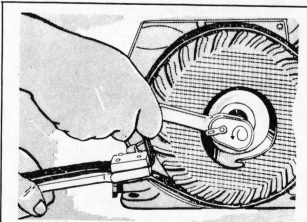

Clinton engine flywheel removal begins with a socket wrench and something to hold the flywheel.

The flywheel can be hammered off like this.

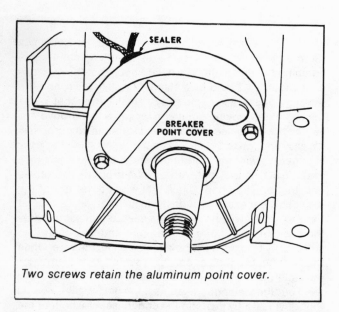

Two screws retain the aluminum point cover.

Clinton engine ignition systems are very similar in design to Briggs & Stratton ignition systems. Flywheels come off in identical fashion, and once off the points and condenser are easily exposed by snapping off the cover and gasket. A worn gasket, by the way, must be replaced. There are differences in detail between Clinton and Briggs engines. You will notice at once that when the flywheel is

Points on Clinton engines are pushed open by removable cams that fit over the crankshaft and are locked into place by a key on the cam. However, Clinton Model 412 and 413 engines have cams that are part of the crankshaft, like Briggs engines in this respect.

Clinton's repair manual predicts a long, carefree life for points and condenser, and about the only time you go trouble-shooting is after prolonged, heavy wear when electrical troubles develop. But once into the point-

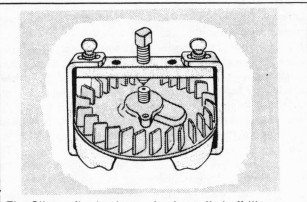

The Clinton flywheel can also be pulled off like this.

condenser housing you need to check for oil in the housing, to check the point gap, which should be .020, and to check the condition of the points themselves. If they show any wear, they should be replaced. If not, put a little grease on the cam and rub it around, then remove any excess.

When installing new points they must match surfaces precisely. Any bending for precise matching must be on the solid point not the movable arm. If surfaces don't match when they touch together you can expect a very short life for the points.

CARBURETION

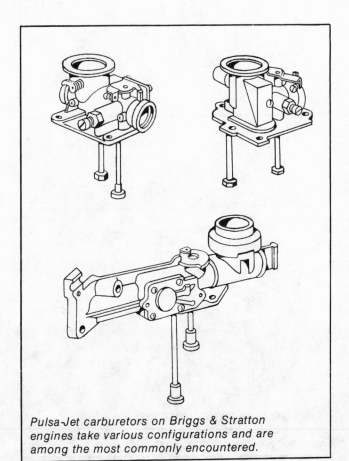

Pulsa-Jet carburetors on Briggs & Stratton engines take various configurations and are among the most commonly encountered.

Carburetors on lawn mowers and all other engines are fairly tricky devices. But, despite the fragility of their parts, and the thin treachery of their adjustments it is surprising how tough and resilient they can be, given half the chance. The point of carburetors is to mix gas and air into the right mix for the highest explosive power in the combustion chamber. It is there, under the spark plug, that the spark plug flame explodes the air-gas mixture — about 15 times as much air as gas — and drive the piston down that turns the crankshaft that turns the mower blade and the wheels, if your mower is self-propelled, and the transmission, then the wheels, if your mower is the riding type.

Before any such explosion can occur, the air-gas mix must not only be precisely right in its proportion, but it must arrive at the precisely right time that is best suited to

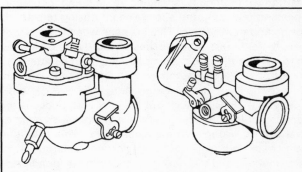

Flo-Jet carburetors have needle valve and float assemblies.

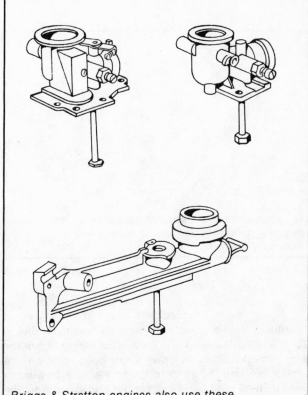

Briggs & Stratton engines also use these Pulsa-Jet and Vacu-Jet carburetors.

the explosion by the spark plug. The valves and timing, points and condenser, magneto and flywheel, must all cooperate in split-second timing if things are to proceed. So, having straightened out the ignition system, we must now proceed to the fuel system, chiefly the carburetor.

Gas from the tank is drawn into the carburetor by some form of fuel pump. This may be a full-blown pump, as in the larger engines, or it may be simply a small suction cup device inside the gas tank-carburetor, or it may be nothing more than gas flowing down hill, into a carburetor lower than the tank. Let us continue to work on the small Briggs & Stratton engines we've been discussing, since that's most likely the one you can't start. The most common carburetor is the Pulsa-Jet, found on Models 82900 and 92900. It is this carburetor that is the culprit when your engine behaves erratically, as noted earlier in this book, starting with difficulty, speeding up, faltering, coughing, speeding up, stuttering and stalling, refusing to start, all for no apparent reason. This happens when the gas tank gets battered out of shape, destroying the seal between carburetor and tank, causing flooding with its attendant symptoms. These symptoms are enough to send you running to the lawn mower supply store for a new gas tank, cost about $8. But check out the tank first, because the tank is not the only thing on these 92000 series engines that can go wrong with the carburetors. Whenever ignition checks out okay but the engine won't start easily or run smoothly and idle correctly, and won't respond properly to acceleration, it's time to dig into the carburetor, probably to clean it out, replace a few parts and reset a few.

To remove the tank-carburetor units on a small Briggs engine requires taking out the two mounting bolts plus linkage.

So we're plagued with the first set of erratic symptoms (above). Two bolts hold the gas tank, one in front, one on the side. The carburetor sitting above the tank is anchored by five thin screw bolts, plus an idle control link and the air vane spring. Remove carburetor and fuel tank together. First, remove the spring from the air vane (that's easily manipulable, flat lever sticking out the side of the engine cover just above the gas tank) and

the large clasp on the accelerator lever — the 4-pronged lever that the throttle cable manipulates from finger controls atop the handlebars. Then unbolt the throttle cable from the front of the engine. This cable is held in place by a claw and small bolt. Use a socket on the bolt to avoid complications. Now you can unbolt the two tank-carburetor bolts (side and front), and pull out the whole unit from its tubes. A metal link rod, from the idle adjustment to the air vane, will be holding the tank-carburetor for dear life. Coax this link out of the idle lever, noting the way it goes back, and now the unit is free.

Take the carburetor off, and be careful with the two fuel pipes dangling below as well as the rubber diaphragm, the spring and its gasket of metal. Using a metal ruler or any perfectly level device, run it across the gas

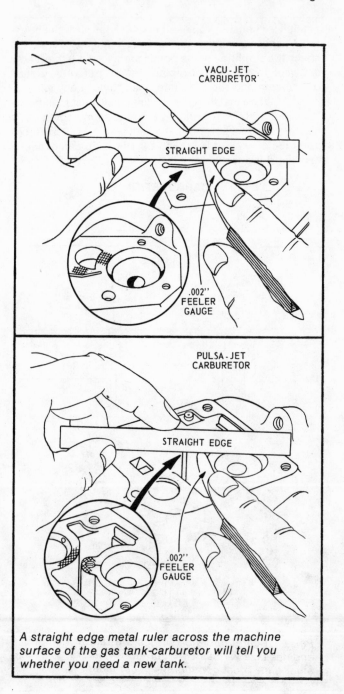

A straight edge metal ruler across the machine surface of the gas tank-carburetor will tell you whether you need a new tank.

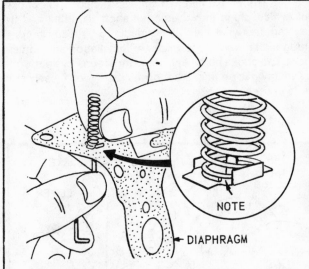

Detail of a Pulsa-Jet diaphragm installation of choke link and spring.

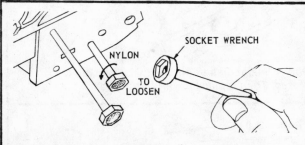

To loosen the nylon pipes use a socket wrench and turn counter-clockwise.

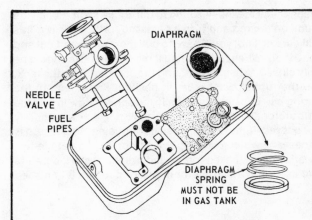

Notice correct sequence of diaphragm spring and metal gasket.

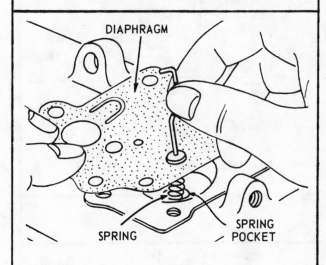

Detail of choke link and spring in diaphragm.

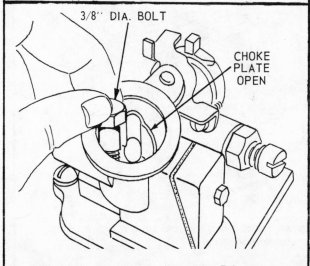

Setting the choke plate in a Pulsa-Jet Briggs engine.

tank slowly and over every opposing two sides of the carburetor area. If there is the slightest sign of warp you must buy a new tank. But even if you can't see any sign of warp, and your carburetor is exhibiting the set of symptoms described above, you need the tank — unless the rubber diaphragm is leaking. Check that out carefully. A wrinkled rubber diaphragm is also cause of replacement.

As to the carburetor itself, look at the little parts that have come out. Blow through the screen at the end of the fuel pipes. If there is any obstruction you'll have to replace them, too. They unscrew with a socket wrench, counter-clockwise. Look at the rubber diaphragm. Unscrew the needle valve and inspect it for dirt or wear. Dirt can be cleaned but wear requires a new one. Wear also means it probably was adjusted incorrectly. Remember, when installing the needle valve that you turn it in gently until it just seats, then turn it back out 1½ turns or two. To clean out the carburetor, if the choke valve sticks or you can see signs of corrosion, requires soaking it in some kind of degreasing fluid like Gunk, for example. But a sticking choke valve can also be caused by purely mechanical means — a bind in the choke shaft. Put a little Gunk on the rod and turn it back and forth. If it is dirt this will cure it. If not you'll have to pull the choke shaft out and sand it off. When re-installing it the plastic valve should be fully closed. When assembling the carburetor on the tank, put the rubber diaphragm in position first, then put the spring cap in place, and finally the spring. Now install the carburetor and tighten the five mounting screws securely but not very tightly, doing them in opposing sequence. It is necessary, when installing the carburetor, to get the two exterior pipes (called intake and breather) started before you can get the carburetor in position to bolt it in place.

The choke mechanism also includes the choke link which plugs into the choke shaft. The link and its housing and what the link connects to beneath the diaphragm all have their folkways of installation and adjustment. The choke being one of the most sensitive performers in any gas engine, it behooves us to look closely at it in its entirety.

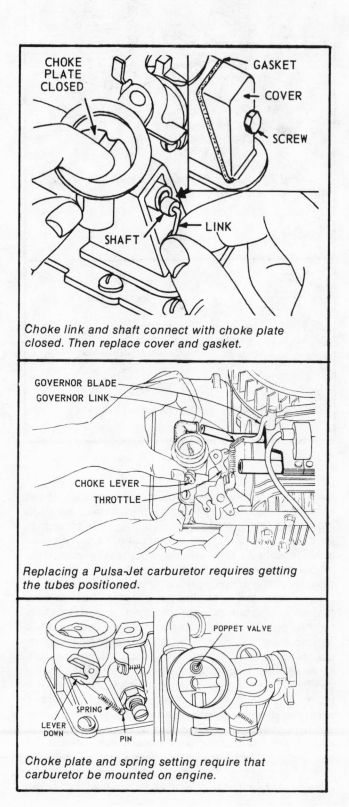

Idle valve and needle valve adjustments on a Pulsa-Jet carburetor.

Choke link connection goes up through hole into connecting chamber.

Choke link and shaft connect with choke plate closed. Then replace cover and gasket.

Replacing a Pulsa-Jet carburetor requires getting the tubes positioned.

Choke plate and spring setting require that carburetor be mounted on engine.

Strictly speaking the choke is an entity unto itself, even though it is an integral part of the carburetor. All fans of auto carburetors will understand this; others may not. What it does is artificially interfere with the best laid plans of the carburetor to send a pre-determined mix of air-gas into the combustion chamber. It declares that the mix needs more air or less air (hence more or less gas) than the pedantic carburetor has decided on. This declaration is based on signals the choke gets from the engine's heat, speed, etc., but above all from the vacuum pressure generated by valves and piston action.

The automatic choke can be checked quickly (nowadays, on Briggs & Stratton, they're all automatic): take off the air cleaner by removing the long screw-bolt; replace the screw-bolt minus the cleaner. The plastic choke valve inside the carburetor throat should be closed all the way. Now move the throttle control lever on the handlebars to "stop." Wind up the starter, let it go and watch the choke valve. It should flutter open and shut, whether or not the engine starts. If your starter is the rope type, pull quickly on the rope, for the same effect. If the choke valve does not react, the choke needs work. Probably, the valve is dirty and sticking, or the choke spring below the diaphragm is not doing its duty.

In Clinton engines the carburetor is usually more complex, the choke less so. It's manually operated. Clinton carburetors are more comparable to automobile carburetors (Clinton gets many of its carburetors from such car carburetor manufacturers as Carter). They all have float systems with needle valves and seats. Needle valves are the chief source of wear and mal-performance because float setting is vital to good engine performance and a worn needle valve changes float setting. Clinton carburetors, with their various passageways (venturi), also may require occasional cleaning. However, the added sophistication of these carburetors also adds stability to their performance. If and when carburetor symptoms appear, after several seasons of normal use, you can be pretty sure that a cleaning of the inside and a new needle valve and seat correctly adjusted will restore performance. There is one exception; the throttle shaft entrance to the carburetor on Clinton's Carter carburetors may wear out — only after prolonged, heavy use — requiring a replacement carburetor. Also, in some models the needle valve seat doesn't come out, and if it is worn the bowl cover, needle pin and spring assembly will have to be replaced. Otherwise, Clinton's carburetors will perform flawlessly for long periods, and their re-building is easy. We'll get to the Clinton carburetor re-building in a moment, but let's go back to the Briggs choke that we left dangling in mid-air.

If the diaphragm spring in the Pulsa-Jet carburetor (all 92000 series excepting 92500) looks okay, it must still be measured. The spring, which is held by tension between two little uprights, should be no less than

Exploded view of a Clinton float type carburetor.

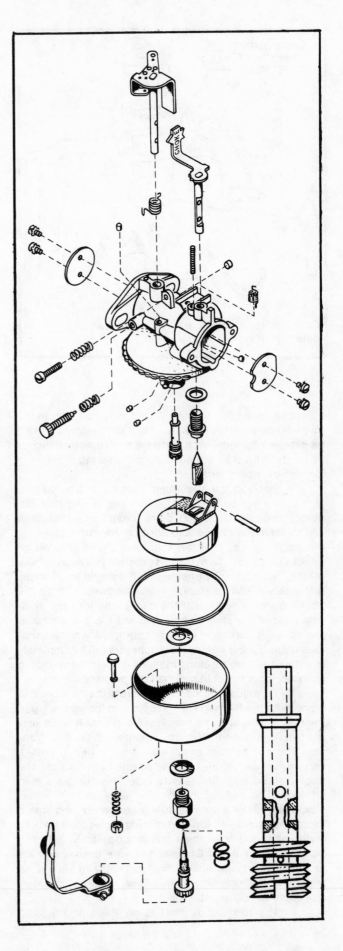

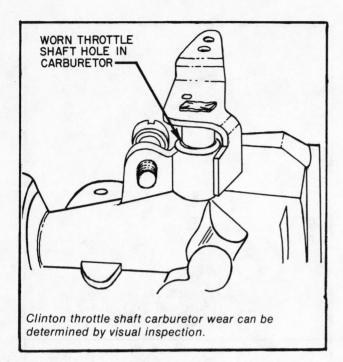

WORN THROTTLE SHAFT HOLE IN CARBURETOR

Clinton throttle shaft carburetor wear can be determined by visual inspection.

screw, which is tucked back underneath. With the engine running, move the throttle to slow position on the handlebars. Now adjust the idle screw until the engine is running at a pretty good clip, but not so that when it is supposed to run in the fast position it overdoes the speed. The specs call for an idle of 1750 r.p.m. That's not terribly slow or fast. Without a tachometer you can't be sure, but it isn't essential. You can check to some extent by moving the throttle control from slow to fast. Acceleration should be smooth. If it wants to quit, either increase the idle speed or change the needle valve to a slightly richer setting.

The large spring controlling the governor or air vane, running from it to the control lever — usually the

1⅛-inches or no more than 1 7/32-inches in length. In the Vacu-Jet carburetors (82500 and 92500) the length should be between 15/16ths-inch and 1-inch maximum. If longer or shorter it must be replaced. Push the spring in between the two clamping surfaces.

Position the diaphragm over the machined surface of the gas tank. Place the cap and spring (the fuel pump) over the recessed pump chamber in the tank (Pulsa-Jet models), and also position the carburetor over the diaphragm so that the automatic choke link will go back into its shaft. To make this possible you need to take off the choke cover by unscrewing the single small screw that holds it and its gasket to the carburetor. With the choke plate closed, push the choke link into the shaft which turns the choke plate. Replace the gasket, cover and screw. If the choke valve isn't completely closed, that means the spring below the diaphragm isn't completely inserted, somewhere along the line (either in the clamping surfaces, or it's rubbing in the tank pocket).

To adjust the carburetor, now that it's back in place, with the five screws that hold it to the tank snug in their beds, you turn the needle valve in until it seats very gently. Then open it 1½ turns (counter-clockwise). Now, start the engine (we assume ignition is okay). With a screwdriver as before turn the needle valve in until the engine slows and threatens to quit. This creates a lean mixture. Then, turn the needle valve out (counter-clockwise) until it begins to run unevenly and again threatens to quit — a too-rich mixture. Now turn it back to midpoint or the smoothest possible operation between rich and lean, like Jack Spratt and his wife, the one who ate only lean meat, the other only fat. The palm should go slightly to the rich side in this case, which is counter-clockwise of mid-point.

The next adjustment is on the idle-adjusting

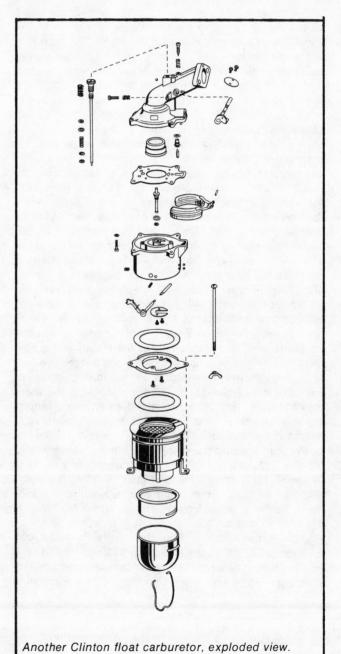

Another Clinton float carburetor, exploded view.

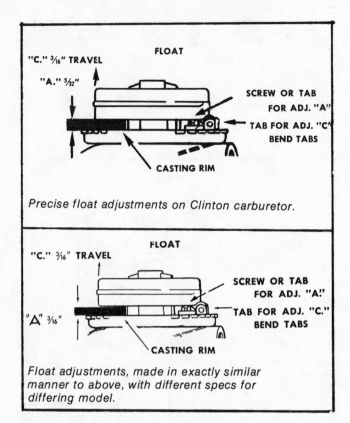

"C." 3/16" TRAVEL
"A." 5/32"

FLOAT

SCREW OR TAB
FOR ADJ. "A"

TAB FOR ADJ. "C"
BEND TABS

CASTING RIM

Precise float adjustments on Clinton carburetor.

"C." 3/16" TRAVEL

FLOAT

SCREW OR TAB
FOR ADJ. "A."

TAB FOR ADJ. "C."
BEND TABS

"A" 3/16"

CASTING RIM

Float adjustments, made in exactly similar manner to above, with different specs for differing model.

float assembly and gasket. Metal parts should be soaked in a cleaner such as Gunk, the gaskets replaced. In 501 engine carburetors the float-needle valve settings go like this: invert bowl cover and with the float resting against the needle pin there should be 13/64-inch clearance between outer edge of bowl cover and the free end of the float — the side opposite from the needle valve seat. You adjust by bending the lip of the float with a small screwdriver.

Continue the assembly now: bowl ring gasket, bowl cover with its drain assembly (opposite side of gas line connection); bolt gasket, bolt assembly; bolt and jet assembly entering bowl; bowl cover gasket; body flange assembly (gas line connection faces you), choke and air intake on the left); upper bolt gasket, washer and bolt lock nut and tighten lock nut; adjusting needle and spring — seat it gently, then open it one turn; air filter, but clean it first if it's metal, if paper get a new one unless the old one is clean; choke assembly with choke valve open.

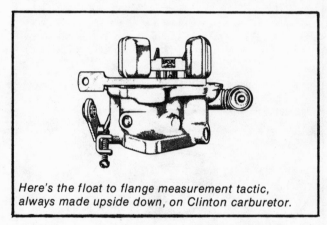

Here's the float to flange measurement tactic, always made upside down, on Clinton carburetor.

post with the largest hole — can cause a lot of trouble if it doesn't have the correct tension. It can interfere with the idle lever as well as fail to do its own job. (Its own job is to keep the engine from running too fast or too slow.) It needs to be taut so as to keep the air vane in position and so as not to sag down on the idle lever and its adjusting screw. If it isn't right, get a new one.

We said that Clinton engines use Carter and other float assembly carburetors, which are all similar in that the float assembly is the key to correct operation and its needle valve is what usually wears and causes what troubles arise. But there is one exception, an interesting "lift carburetor" which doesn't use the float assembly. This carburetor is not one you are likely to encounter in any case, but if you do we strongly urge you to leave it alone. It's much too complicated a gadget to play with, and requires a lot of unusual service tactics.

The float assembly carburetors, found on virtually all Clintons, beginning with their smallest 2-cycle engine (the type that mixes oil with gas for fuel and lubrication), should not be taken apart unless these symptoms arise: idle can't be controlled; engine balks, won't accelerate properly; is difficult to start; engine surges and runs unevenly; carburetor leaks. In general, these troubles will be cured with a thorough cleaning out, replacing the needle valve and re-setting it, and replacing any worn gaskets. The order of disassembly is to unhook the controls, then remove carburetor from engine. Air filter and choke assembly are next. Then upper body and gasket which are held by a bolt, lock nut, and washer. Then the lower body assembly and cover gasket, the jet assembly and gasket, the bowl and bowl drain (if any). Finally, the float pin, the

Clinton LMG, LMB, and LMV type carburetors are all float types. They are similar to the one we've talked about but sufficiently different to note their parts breakdown. First remove the air cleaner assembly. This is a dry element cleaner with a poly-foam band that fits over the element in some models. Once you remove the carburetor from the engine, after removing the throttle link, and the several bolts, you want to remove only the upper half in order to get at the needle valve and float assembly. But if the carburetor looks dirty, when you take off the top of it, you'll have to continue the process of taking it apart in order to soak it in de-greaser. In that case, remove the gasket over the bowl, the idle adjusting needle and spring, the throttle valve screws, valve and throttle (but only if it sticks).

The new needle valve assembly must be adjusted. It includes a needle valve seat, gasket and float pin or shaft if it comes with the rebuilding kit. To set the float assembly, invert the casting and assembly. You want a space of 5/32 inch between the outer rim of the casting and the nearest part of the float at the end farthest from the hinge. The end of the float, in other words, should seat 5/32 inch from the rim of the bowl. If it does not, an adjusting tab that

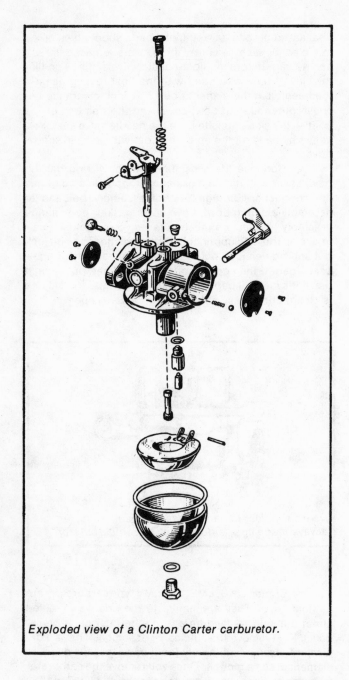

Exploded view of a Clinton Carter carburetor.

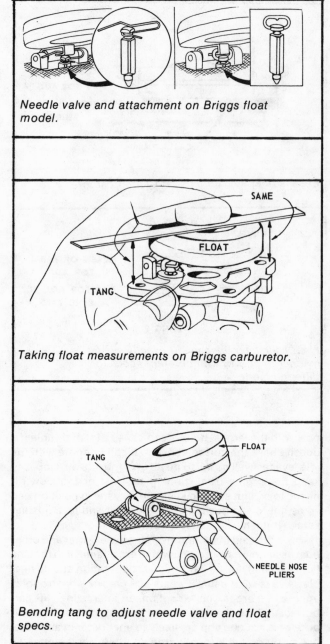

Needle valve and attachment on Briggs float model.

Taking float measurements on Briggs carburetor.

Bending tang to adjust needle valve and float specs.

will do the trick is at the hinge. Bend the tab that rests against the float valve with a screwdriver. That done, turn the bowl over to normal position. The float should not fall more the 3/16 inch. In back of the hinge is another tab to bend and set the float drop to no more than that figure. Note: in some of these models there is an adjusting screw for the first adjustment. That, of course, simplifies matters. Now replace any other parts you took off — you should keep dis-assembly to a minimum, but you will want to use a new bowl gasket. All float carburetors have similar problems and components, though they may differ in this or that detail. But if you've adjusted one float assembly you can adjust them all. The needle valve seat — the circular receptacle for the needle valve with its tapered end to drop into and shut off or open up the gas flow — should

usually be replaced when changing the needle valve, unless it is specifically designed into the bowl and is not replaceable. (Not many like that.)

Governor controls

We've talked about the air vane or governor on the Briggs & Stratton engines. If this is incorrectly installed, or the spring gets distorted, the engine won't behave properly, either in starting or in general performance. The air vane spring has double end loops and it must be removed whenever you do carburetor and/or engine work. See illustrations on facing page for correct removal and installation.

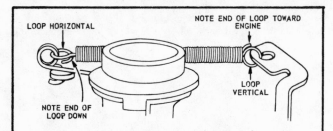

Normal installation of air vane spring on Briggs governor.

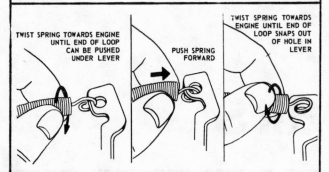

Removal of air vane spring from control lever.

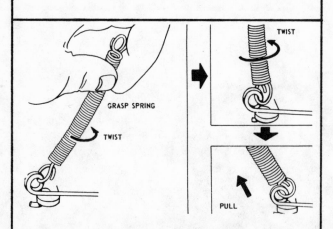

Removal of air vane spring from air vane link.

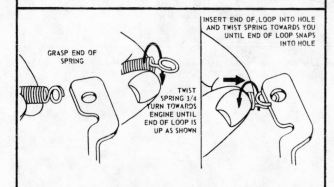

Replacement of air vane spring into control lever.

Note that the air vane side of the spring installation goes into the idle link which in turn goes into the air vane. Not the other way around. If you get them crossed you'll have starting trouble. The link first, the air vane spring into it.

On larger Briggs & Stratton engines the Remote Governor control changes spring tension and regulates engine speed by controlling the carburetor throttle at all times.

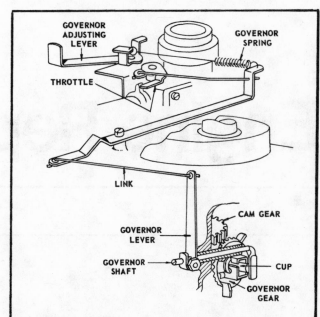

Governor links, spring and controls on Briggs engine.

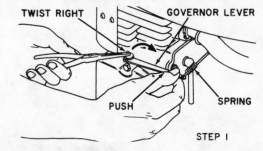

Tecumseh governor linkage adjustment involves these steps.

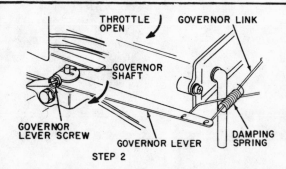

Governor adjustments on Tecumseh engines are made with lever screw.

Chapter Two

Engine Repairs

Every season or two, depending on use, it is well to remove the cylinder head and clean out the carbon. In the process it is also a good idea to test engine compression — vacuum seal and thrust through valves and piston, combustion chamber, head gasket, etc. After you have removed the starter mechanism, exposing the crankshaft and flywheel, spin the flywheel counter-clockwise a couple of times. If it rebounds sharply this means compression is normal. If it is weak or wan, compression is similarly below par. That means, probably, the valves need re-surfacing and re-seating, a job you may or may not wish to undertake — though it's not difficult. You can check compression without removing the starter mechanism by removing the spark plug cable, making sure it can't touch the plug, then turning the blade underneath counter-clockwise. This, of course, poses the possibility of risk from the blade and is recommended only if you pull the blade with some kind of extension — a long vise pliers or some such thing that will keep your hands away from the blade.

To remove the head for cleaning out carbon from the combustion chamber requires removing also the shield and whatever keeps it. Also, begin by removing the spark plug and noting its condition. In the Briggs small engine series (92000 models, and others), the cylinder is aluminum. Cast iron cylinders are found on larger Briggs engines. Clinton engines are also aluminum in the 3-h.p. models.

Eight engine bolts hold the cylinder head. You will notice that three of the bolts are longer than the others. If you can't remember which ones go where, mark the tops with chalk.

Also, you will notice that these bolts are not heavily torqued (tightened). Aluminum doesn't withstand as much tightening as cast iron, so govern yourself accord-ingly when assembling head, gasket and shield. Notice also that when the head comes off the cylinder gasket also comes off easily, unlike car engine head gaskets which are cemented and mostly need scraping off. When putting the head gasket back, DON'T use any gasket cement on it. Also, you can generally re-use the old one, if it has no cracks in it, looks to be in good health, and you get it back in precisely the same position as you found it. All mechanics recommend using new gaskets every time you expose a gasket, but if you don't happen to have a new one and are anxious to use the mower you'll find that the old one, properly installed and showing no cracks or defects, will work perfectly well. At least, it will work long enough to hunt up a new one.

To clean carbon off the piston, valves and cylinder head, use a screwdriver. There are carbon scrapers but you can do as well with a couple of screwdrivers. Just don't be too vigorous about it. Piston and other combustion chamber surfaces are easily scratched and marred. You're only out to clean, not to perform surgery. If you gouge soft metal you change combustion chamber specifications. This will not improve engine performance, and that's the point of this operation, whereas cleaning out carbon will give the engine a noticeable lift, all other systems being up to it.

When re-installing the head, get the gasket back as before, and the shield. Then finger-tighten each bolt. Next, making sure that the long bolts are where they belong, tighten each bolt lightly, just making sure that it seats. There is a correct order to tightening cylinder head bolts — it goes like this; No. 1 at the left, No. 2 at the middle right (opposite No. 1), No. 3 bottom right, No. 4 top left, No. 5 top right, No. 6 bottom left, No. 7 bottom center, No. 8 top center. (We're again speaking of Briggs 92000 series engines.) Clinton engines are different; the order is No. 1, top

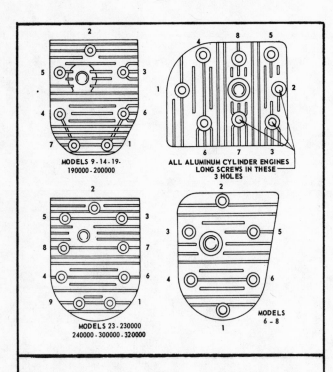

MODELS 9 - 14 - 19 -
190000 - 200000

ALL ALUMINUM CYLINDER ENGINES
LONG SCREWS IN THESE
3 HOLES

MODELS 23 - 230000
240000 - 300000 - 320000

MODELS
6 - 8

BASIC MODEL SERIES	IN. LBS. TORQUE
ALUMINUM CYLINDER	
6B, 60000, 8B, 80000 82000, 92000 100000, 130000	140
140000, 170000, 190000	165
CAST IRON CYLINDER	
5, 6, N, 8, 9	140
14	165
19, 190000, 200000, 23, 230000, 240000, 300000, 320000	190

Briggs engine heads should be loosened and tightened according to the numbers and models above, and according to the torque specs in above table.

TORQUE IN NUMERICAL ORDER

TORQUE TO 200 INCH LBS. IN 50 INCH LB. INCREMENTS

A Tecumseh engine head tightening and loosening sequence, with torque.

TORQUE IN NUMERICAL ORDER

TORQUE TO 200 INCH LBS. IN 50 INCH LB. INCREMENTS

Another Tecumseh head torque, loosening and tightening spec series.

right, then proceed clockwise around the head (around the spark plug hole), tightening gently at first, and going around three times, the third time being the charm.

If you have access to a torque wrench you might get the tightening a little more precise. On the Briggs engines we're talking about, the torque is 140 inch-pounds. Not all torque wrenches measure inch-pounds, by the way. You can't use a foot-pound wrench. And if you use a torque wrench don't bull ahead with it and tighten the first bolt all the way to 140 inch-pounds, the second ditto, etc. That would distort the head and maybe even ruin it. Head bolts and other machined surface multi-bolt installations must always be approached gingerly when it comes time to tighten; always begin by finger tightening, then start to draw up bolts, usually opposite each other unless it is specified clockwise or counter-clockwise as in the Clinton series. Even if the machined surface has only two bolts

you should still tighten them with the same approach. Allow three tightens per bolt, before attaining maximum torque.

If, in the compression test you made, twisting the crankshaft counter-clockwise, you got no response, you must now look to valves and rings. But first, the compression test must be made in the compression cycle of the engine. In Briggs engines there are three other cycles, and so you must do the test at least four times, because in three cycles you won't get the correct response. Compression loss is caused by a faulty head gasket, which you can see by inspection of it carefully; by valves sticking, burned or not seating; by piston rings failing, which means engine oil consumption to an excessive degree. Indeed, these engines shouldn't consume any oil, though they may lose oil through leakage. Of course, the two cycle engines by Clinton use oil mixed with gas in the fuel system.

You can begin by visually inspecting the valves

and their seating. If heavy carbon formation has built up around the valves you can be certian of valve leakage. If there's carbon on the underside of the valve head it means valve guide leak. And if the rings are allowing oil you can expect not only very heavy carbon deposits in the combustion chamber — on the cylinder head itself, but heavily flaked over the piston, with burning evidence at the top of the piston well, and on the spark plug too. If you suspect the valves of mal-functioning you will need to buy an inexpensive valve lifting tool, to compress the valve spring enough to release the valve pin, collars and retainer. The valve tool fits above and below the spring, and compresses it. You can improvise a valve tool using a screwdriver, vise pliers and other tools, but if you're going to do the valves the lifting tool is cheap and much easier on the nerves, the hands and the valve spring.

makes valve spring compressors for its several engine models. The problem shown by the different compressors is that a very small space is available in which to use any tool to compress the spring, and auto engines usually (but not invariably) give you more space in which to maneuver, hence the specialized problem of the small 1-cylinder engine. Also, that's why you can't use your friendly auto valve compressor.

In using the valve spring compressor you want to avoid damaging or distorting the valve spring in any way. Though it's a rather tough spring it isn't beyond ruining. There are, by the way, two springs, one for the intake and one for the exhaust valve, and they aren't necessarily identical. So they must be kept separate, and returned to their original places.

The valve spring compressor fits over the top of

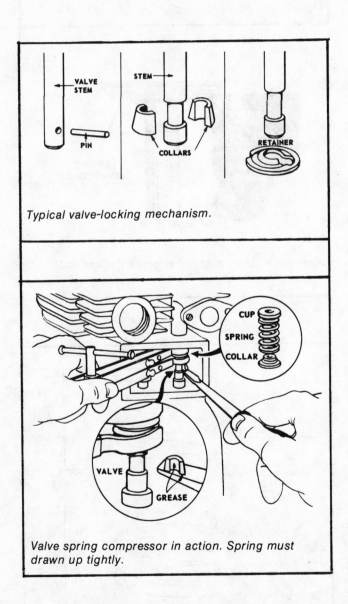

Typical valve-locking mechanism.

Valve spring compressor in action. Spring must drawn up tightly.

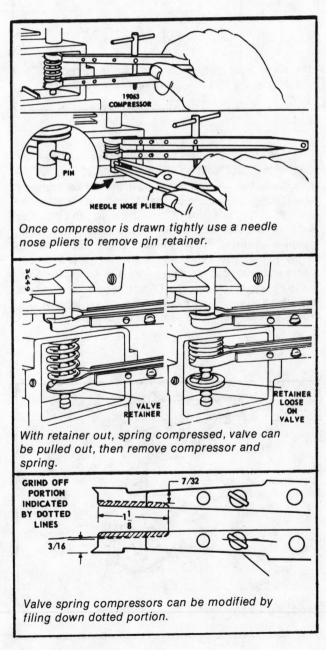

Once compressor is drawn tightly use a needle nose pliers to remove pin retainer.

With retainer out, spring compressed, valve can be pulled out, then remove compressor and spring.

Valve spring compressors can be modified by filing down dotted portion.

Note: Briggs & Stratton sells a jawed valve spring compressor designed specifically for these small engines. A regular auto valve compressor won't fit. Clinton also the valve chamber and the lower jaw of the compressor fits between spring and retainer. Compress the spring and you can them remove the retainer, and whatever else keeps the valve locked in. Then you can remove the valve, the compressor and spring, in that order.

Valves can be re-surfaced, though you are best advised to take them to a lawn mower shop for the purpose. It is probably best to buy new valves and have the seats re-surfaced.

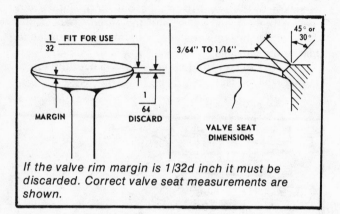

If the valve rim margin is 1/32d inch it must be discarded. Correct valve seat measurements are shown.

Before valves are re-installed they must be "lapped" into proper seating. That consists of placing the valve in position without installing it, then smearing some valve lapping compound on the opposing surfaces of the valve face (the underside of the valve head) and the valve seat — what it closes on in the combustion chamber. Then the valve is whirled about by hand, using a lapping tool or simply an inexpensive toy-like gadget with a suction cup at one end, until both surfaces are polished and smooth. But avoid too much lapping. Clinton recommends a light re-working via lapping because too much lapping can produce a rounded valve seat and a distorted valve face.

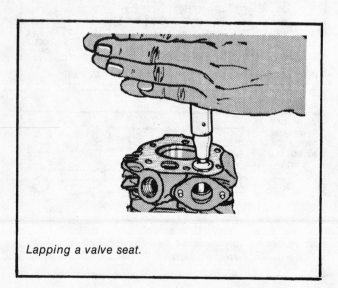

Lapping a valve seat.

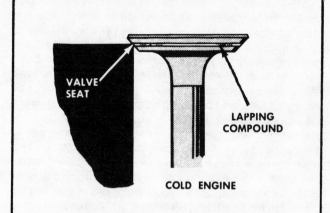

Valves must seat in both cold and hot engines. Here's procedure for lapping cold engine valve.

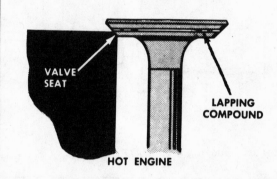

Procedure for lapping hot engine valve and seat. Lap lightly, not energetically.

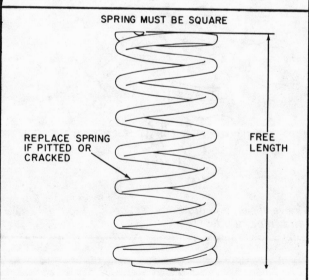

Replace any valve spring that shows imperfections of surface, balance and length.

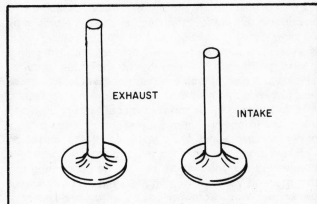

Tecumseh engine exhaust and intake valves.

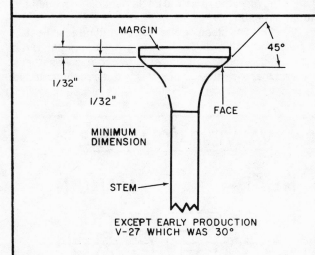

Tecumseh valve specs.

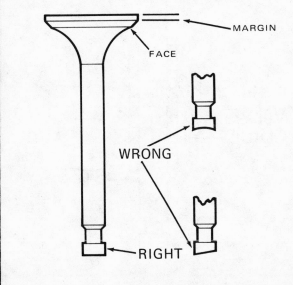

If the valve stem needs grinding off there's only one right way to do it.

So take it very easy with the lapping bit. All you want to do is remove any possible surface blemishes. Then you must clean every bit of lapping compound away with kerosene or some such cleaner.

When the valve is lapped you must next make certain that the gap between the valve stem and the tappet that opens it is correct. The tappet, which is pushed by the camshaft, must have a slight clearance between it and the valve stem. Use the feeler gauge to measure it. Insufficient clearance between tappet and stem will prevent a full closing of the valve (either valve); too great a clearance will discombobulate the opening and closing of the valve — throw it off timing. Small engines that we're talking about — Briggs 92000, 82000, etc. — have different tappet clearance schedules, as shown in the table nearby. From the highest position of each valve, turn one revolution of camshaft and check. A new valve, whether exhaust or intake, will undoubtedly be longer than the old and will have to be ground off. Put the new valve in a vise and file it off — but very precisely.

The new valve won't be any better than the valve seat, and if the seat is burned or worn it will be necessary to have the seat replaced. You can see whether the seat is burned — it will be the exhaust valve seat not the intake — but you can't see entirely whether the seat is not going to close precisely until you lap the valve and seat together. Also, you can't see whether the valve guide, through which the valve stem descends, leaks oil. Valves, stem, face, pistons and rings all work together (along with the head and gasket) to create proper compression, and any one of these elements that becomes worn or distorted can upset the delicate balances at issue. The toughest pressure is on the exhaust valve, which is under temperatures of several thousand degrees, and if it breaks down it proceeds to weaken the rest of the system. Rings, nowadays, are made of sufficiently tough metal, unlike earlier times, so that they aren't likely to be first to defect. But you never know. Murphy's law applies here — "anything that can go wrong will."

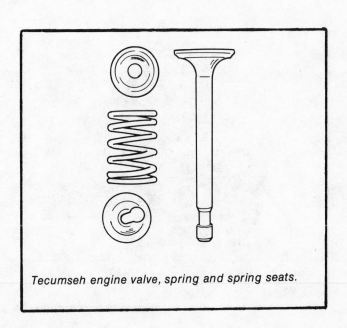

Tecumseh engine valve, spring and spring seats.

To re-install valves, place spring and retainer and whatever else is involved in the valve train — some models have a cup at the top of the spring and a collar at the bottom — into the valve spring compressor and tighten the compressor until the spring is solid. Then place the compressed spring, retainer, etc., into the chamber. Next, drop the valve into place, threading the valve stem through the retainer, insert the retainer pin or place the collars in the groove of the valve stem — whichever applies. Lower the spring until the retainer fits around the pin or the collars. Then release the spring compressor. Check to make sure the pin and/or the collars are in place. Some retainers are self-locking devices and go in (and out) somewhat differently. Clinton engines have valve keepers, shaped like a C. Also, some Clinton engines are sneaky; they develop small burrs on the valve stem lock that must be filed off before the valve will come out of the guide hole. This is easy enough to do; take a flat file and hold it against the burred area, then rotate the valve sufficiently to remove the burr.

Valve guides can be measured by a valve guide plug gauge, which you are not likely to have or be able to borrow, but you can compare the way the old valve slipped through the guide with the way the new one does. If the old one is loose, the new one snug, you can expect the new valve to prevent oil leakage. You can't make the necessary repairs to the valve guide without a reamer and drill press. So, if the new valve doesn't fit closely you'll have to have the guide bored and a valve guide bushing installed. This will be required only with heavy, prolonged usage, but since it's a possibility it shouldn't be overlooked.

Note: valve springs lose their tension. If the spring isn't straight, or you think it has lost its tension — you can begin a test by comparing exhaust and intake springs with each other; they should be the same size and tension, even when one of them is slightly thicker — you need to buy a new spring. Buy two new ones; they're inexpensive, compared to the labor you use to extract and replace them.

If piston rings and piston pin are suspected — if the engine burns a lot of oil and has the symptoms of oil burning in the combustion chamber outlined above — it is necessary to consider removing the piston and installing new rings. This job, like the valve job above, also requires at least one special tool, a ring compressor which, needless to say, is totally unlike the valve spring compressor. And if the piston cylinder walls turn out to be scored, and you want to re-bore them yourself, you'll need a fairly expensive special tool, additionally. You'll also need some skill. On Briggs engines, to remove the piston and its connecting rod you'll find a cap on the connecting rod that prevents you from getting a wrench over one side of the screw. With a screwdriver or a punch and hammer, flatten out this cap, then unscrew the two retaining bolts. Remove the cap. Before you push the piston and rod out through the top of the cylinder you must scrape off or ream off any carbon and/or ridge at the top of the cylinder, well. Otherwise, the rings will be damaged. Then push out the piston and rod.

You can clean off the carbon and ridge at the top of the cylinder, if it isn't extensive, with sandpaper, but if it's markedly ridged you'll have to beg, borrow or steal a ridge reamer. Needless to say, this is not a recommended

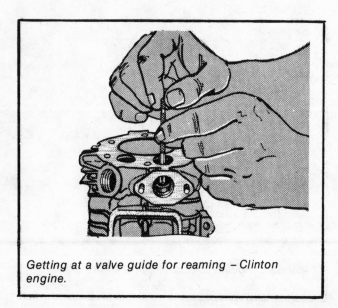

Getting at a valve guide for reaming – Clinton engine.

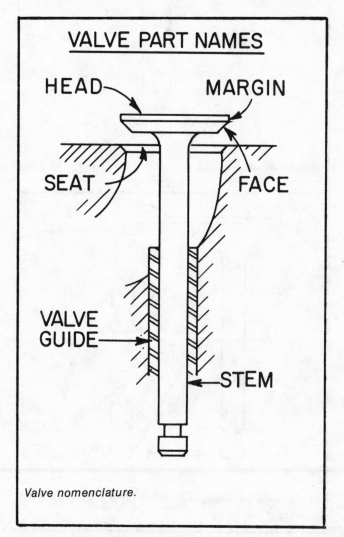

Valve nomenclature.

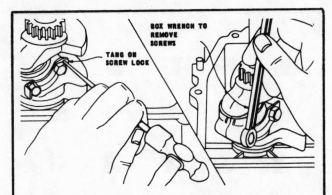

On Briggs engines you have to flatten out tangs on the connecting rod at the crankshaft before you can unbolt the rod.

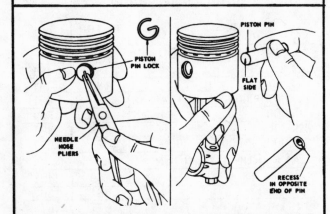

Piston pin locks come out with needle nose pliers. On Briggs engines the pin has different configurations at each end.

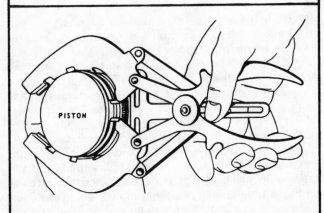

Piston ring removal tool.

investment in view of the scarcity of opportunity to use it. (However, the same reamer will work on an auto engine, if that's in the picture.) They're not very expensive.

To get the connecting rod off the piston, pull out the piston pin lock, using a thin nosed pliers — one end of the pin is designed to grab hold of, the other isn't.

If the piston looks okay you still have to check out the ring grooves. To do this remove the rings. Since the engine has been burning oil and you plan to install new rings, you don't need to be over-protective of the old ones. But you must either be scientific in removing them — that is, use a special tool designed for the job — or careful. Don't forget; rings break very easily. They're fragile, like eggshells. But they can also score the fairly delicate piston. So, you must fish them out gently, and coax them over the ring "lands" taking great care to avoid scratches. The way you do this, if you don't have the special tool, is to fish one end up and slowly extricate the entire ring using a small screwdriver. Then pull the ends slightly apart and work the ring off, either up or down depending on its position — the upper rings are most easily removed above, the lower rings pushed off the lower part of the

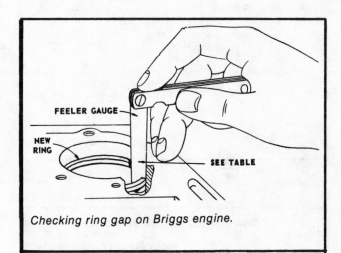

Checking ring gap on Briggs engine.

RING GAP REJECTION SIZE		
BASIC MODEL SERIES	COMP. RING	OIL RING
ALUMINUM CYLINDER		
6B, 60000, 8B, 80000		
82000, 92000		
100000, 130000	.035	.045
140000, 170000, 190000		
CAST IRON CYLINDER		
5, 6, 8, N, 9		
14, 19, 190000		
200000, 23	.030	.035
230000, 240000		
300000, 320000		

piston. To check out the piston, scrape the carbon from the top ring groove, then place a new ring in the groove — at any clean point, (don't install it, just push an edge into the groove, and try to push a .007 feeler gauge into the groove with the new ring). If the gauge goes in you must buy a new piston — the old one is worn out. Buy a chrome ring set, and follow the installation instructions.

These instructions will explain that the rings must be installed with a ring compressor. This is not wholly true. If you take great care you can get them in without breaking them. But this is a ticklish decision, and if you can borrow or rent a compressor by all means do so. In any case, the ring compressor is inexpensive — a dollar or two.

But there are two things you must do, before installing the new rings. First, make sure the piston is cleaned and the oil holes in the ring grooves fully open. Use one of the old rings to clean out the grooves; use a

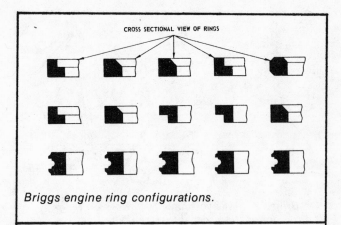

Briggs engine ring configurations.

PISTON PIN REJECTION SIZES

BASIC MODEL SERIES	PISTON PIN	PIN BORE
ALUMINUM CYLINDER		
6B, 60000	.489	.491
8B, 80000	.489	.491
82000, 92000	.489	.491
100000	.552	.554
130000	.489	.491
140000, 170000, 190000	.671	.671
CAST IRON CYLINDER		
5, 6, 8, N	.489	.491
9	.561	.563
14, 19, 190000	.671	.673
200000	.671	.673
23, 230000	.734	.736
240000	.671	.673
300000, 320000	.799	.801

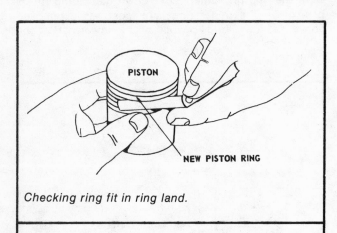

Checking ring fit in ring land.

CONNECTING ROD REJECT SIZES

BASIC MODEL SERIES	CRANK PIN BEARING	PISTON PIN BEARING
ALUMINUM CYLINDER		
6B, 60000	.876	.492
8B, 80000	1.0013	.492
82000, 92000	1.0013	.492
100000	1.0013	.555
130000	1.0013	.492
140000, 170000	1.0949	.674
190000	1.1265	.674
CAST IRON CYLINDER		
5	.7524	.492
6, 8. N	.751	.492
9	.876	.5633
14, 19, 190000	1.0007	.6735
200000	1.1265	.6735
23, 230000	1.189	.736
240000	1.314	.6735
300000, 320000	1.314	.8015

drill bit on the oil holes in the grooves. Second, you need to oil the rings and the piston with motor oil before proceeding to the installation of the rings.

Each of the rings has its own function and they are different in design. The bottom ring, an oil ring, takes an expander ring beneath it, if the top of your piston has an "L" stamped on it. If not, no expander. The expander, which is simply a spring to impart tension to the oil ring, goes on first. The two rings above are compression rings, so-called, but each is different and must be not mixed up. Installation with a ring compressor requires that you place the rings in their proper grooves, staggering the ring ends so that all the openings are not in line, otherwise compression will be lost. Then, with the compressor installed over the rings, place the piston through the cylinder, turn upside down and force down on the compressor, loosening it a tiny bit if it doesn't want to yield. Don't loosen it to the point where the rings can be sheared off.

When replacing the piston onto the connecting rod push the pin lock in at the opening with a pliers. The

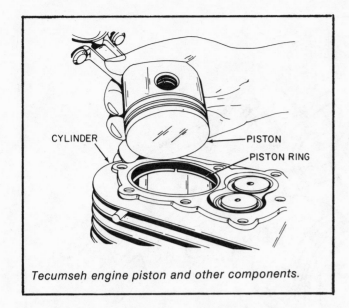

Tecumseh engine piston and other components.

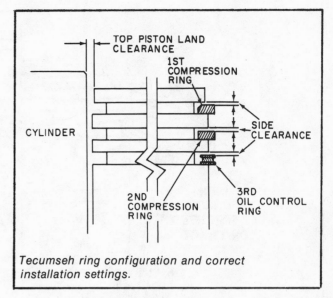

Tecumseh ring configuration and correct installation settings.

pin lock is a wire, circular device. With the lock in place, push the pin through against the lock, then install a lock on the other end. Now look at the lower end of the connecting rod and its bearing surface — the surface that turns on the crankshaft. If it is not smooth — if it is scored or shows any sign of irregular wear it (the connecting rod) must be replaced. Whether replacing or using the same

rod it is important to keep dirt away from the surfaces. It is also important that fresh oil be placed on the surfaces before joining them.

If your model has an "F" on the piston the "F" should face the flywheel side of the engine. Otherwise, push the piston and connecting rod down into the cylinder so it meets the crankshaft and assemble the two so

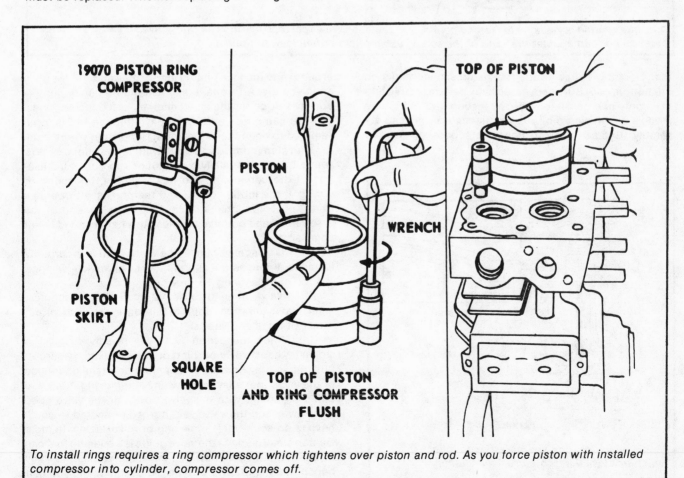

To install rings requires a ring compressor which tightens over piston and rod. As you force piston with installed compressor into cylinder, compressor comes off.

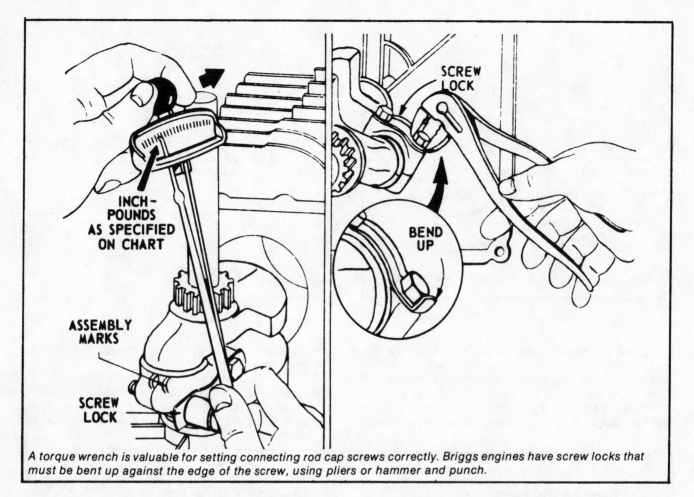

INCH-POUNDS AS SPECIFIED ON CHART

ASSEMBLY MARKS

SCREW LOCK

SCREW LOCK

BEND UP

A torque wrench is valuable for setting connecting rod cap screws correctly. Briggs engines have screw locks that must be bent up against the edge of the screw, using pliers or hammer and punch.

that assembly marks on the rod match similar marks on the bottom cap. But some assemblies have no marks and fit in only one possible way. You'll soon find out. Some models also have an oil dipper attached to this cap assembly. Replace the oil dipper (it scoops oil up and

NOTCH

LETTER "F"

TOP RING

CENTER RING

ASSEMBLY MARKS   FLYWHEEL SIDE

Some Briggs pistons are marked with letter "F" which is a visual aid to correct installation.

around) and the lock plate. Tighten the cap screws tightly and securely. A torque wrench would be handy here — correct torque for the small engines is 100 inch-pounds. But you can guess at it if you pay attention to the force required to open the cap screws. Remember you're dealing with aluminum so you don't want to over-tighten. Now rotate the crankshaft two revolutions to check installation. If the connecting rod hits anything, the rod is in wrong. If the job is correct and the crankshaft operates freely, push the lock surface up against the end of the screw head and pound it closed with a hammer and tap of some sort.

If, by some chance, the crankshaft is incorrectly installed, it means the align marks don't match. Change the rod cap assembly so they do.

We've been discussing small Briggs engines; similar considerations apply to Clinton, in the removal and repair of rings and valves.

When inspection of valves reveals suspicious signs—exhaust valve burning on the edge, heavy carbon build-up in the combustion chamber or on the underside of the valve (not easy to see without removing it but you can see enough with the valve open), or the valve edge worn away and the valve seat burned or scored — you'll have to do some valve replacing or re-surfacing. In most Clinton small engines the valve guide is a bushing that can be pushed out and a new one installed. You can use any punch that fits to drive out the old bushing, and you can drive the new one in — but with care. Unless you have some method of forcing the new bushing in without damaging it, you'd better get it to a machine shop for pressing. And if that, have them press the old one out, while you're at it.

Valves in 2-cycle Clinton engines differ from 4-cylinder engines. If your mower is a 2-cycle, and you suspect it of valve trouble — the troubles are the same as those already described — you can easily enough replace the valves.

Clinton pistons, rings, and rods are more or less identical, though the rings themselves are slightly different from those specified for Briggs engines. But, they come off and go on exactly the same. When installing rings Clinton recommends its own system. The oil ring (at the bottom) has an expander which, of course, goes on first. Then, the oil ring, which can go either way, is installed. Next the "scraper" ring (in the middle), which has a

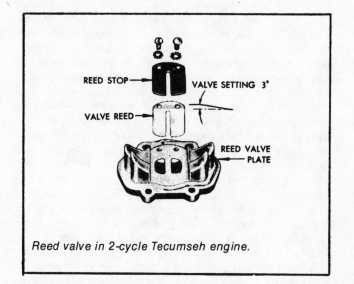

Reed valve in 2-cycle Tecumseh engine.

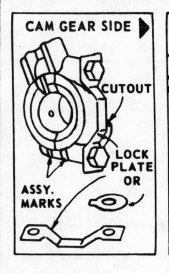

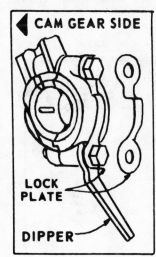

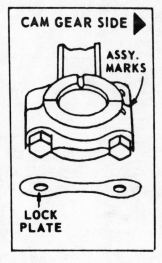

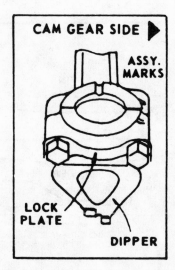

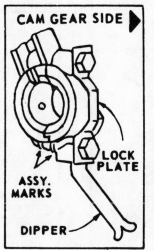

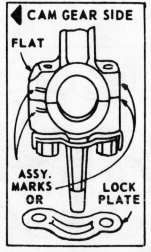

Connecting rods on Briggs engines lock with plate or tang. Assembly marks guide correct installation of rod, locking plate and oil dipper, when present.

"step" machined out of the lower outer circumference, and this step should face downward. Stagger the rings so that the opening of this ring does not line up with either opening above and below it (oil ring below; compression ring above). Now, the top or compression ring, has a 45-degree bevel on the upper inner circumference, which should point upward to the top of the piston. When the rings are installed, they should have free movement in their grooves. Check the ring to groove clearance; 2-cycle engines minimum is .0015, maximum .004; 4-cycle engines (below 5 h.p.) minimum, .002; maximum .005. If the piston doesn't measure up to these tolerances it must be replaced.

Connecting rods should be inspected for scuffing and discoloration, and for cracks on the bearing surfaces (at both ends of the rod); if any of these defects are visible the rod should be replaced. In replacing the piston in 4-cycle Clinton engines, the piston may go either way, but the rod has an oil hole that must face toward the flywheel side of the engine. Some Clinton engines have a specially designed connecting rod with a "clearance side" that is shaped differently from the other side and is marked. This side is installed toward the camshaft of the engine. But on 2-cycle Clinton engines the piston must be installed so that the high, built-up side of the piston top goes toward the intake valve side of the block. But the rod goes in either way.

It is not recommended that you go digging into crankshaft removal. But if you must (if the engine vibrates excessively, for example) first remove the oil sump, which has bolts and a heavy gasket that will probably stick — and must be replaced with a new one. Then — and this is crucial — once the take-off end is removed and before you pull out the crankshaft, rotate it until its timing mark (a chisel mark) is aligned with a mark on the camshaft gear. Then you can pull it out, along with the cam gear, and get it back in timing, so that the engine will work. Otherwise, you'll spend forever in a hit and miss search for timing. If you are getting engine vibration and you suspect the crankshaft — a sound suspicion — and have ruled out the blade, there is a table of crankshaft reject sizes (in inches) that will confirm the need or lack of it for a new crankshaft.

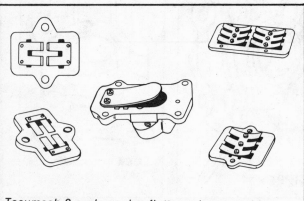

Tecumseh 2-cycle engine flutter valve assembly and components.

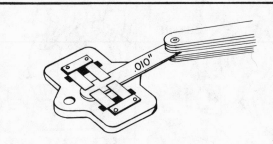

Measuring flutter valve specs with feeler gauge.

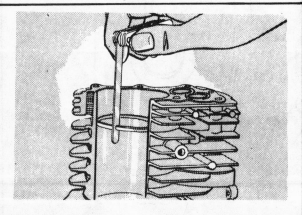

Checking ring gap on Clinton engine with feeler gauge.

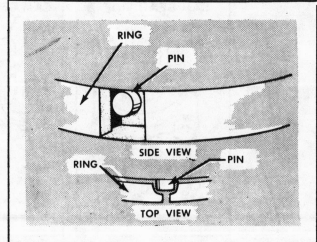

Details of Clinton piston ring setting and pin.

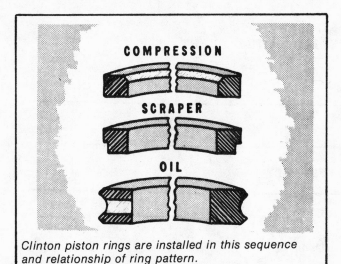

Clinton piston rings are installed in this sequence and relationship of ring pattern.

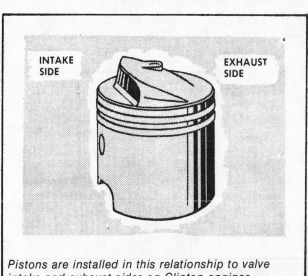

OIL HOLE

Clinton installation of piston and rod showing oil hole as a guide to correct placement.

The way you check out the blade, to see whether it is the guilty party or not, is to remove it, then run the engine. If the engine continues to vibrate it's the crankshaft; if not, you only need a new blade. Needless to say, this simplifies matters enormously. You can check the blade yourself, by balancing it and if it does not balance exactly it's bad. But it might be best to take it to a lawn mower shop because you'll have to buy a new one if it is, and if it isn't you can get a professional sharpening job. A blade that causes vibration is a candidate either for replacement or professional sharpening.

If you have removed the crankshaft, and if you replace it with a new one, you should know that it has a certain amount of end play. Installation procedure begins with the valve tappets first, the crankshaft next, finally the cam gear. Crankshaft and cam gear timing marks must align — that's the way you install them. Not all small engine Briggs models have timing marks on the crankshaft (and timing gear). Engines in which the crankshafts have ball bearings have timing marks on the counterweight of the crankshaft and on the cam gear. So, you align the cam gear mark with the mark on the crankshaft counterweight. End play on all models is .002 inch to .008 inch. If less than .002 with a new crankcase or sump — and that would definitely be the case with a new sump or new crankcase — you can get thrust washers to correct the end play. Thus, this situation — less than .002 — requires additional gaskets of .005, .009, or .015 in selected combinations, to obtain the desired specification. If end play is

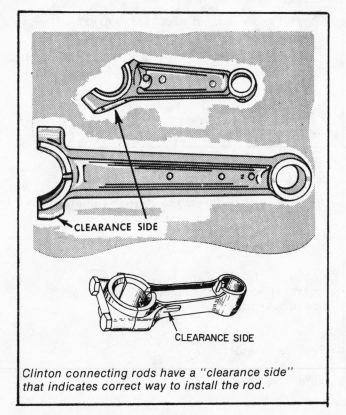

CLEARANCE SIDE

CLEARANCE SIDE

Clinton connecting rods have a "clearance side" that indicates correct way to install the rod.

INTAKE SIDE   EXHAUST SIDE

Pistons are installed in this relationship to valve intake and exhaust sides on Clinton engines.

2-CYCLE ENGINE TROUBLESHOOTING CHART

Cause	Remedy
ENGINE FAILS TO START OR STARTS WITH DIFFICULTY	
No fuel in tank	Fill tank with clean, fresh fuel.
Fuel shut-off valve closed	Open valve.
Obstructed fuel line	Clean fuel screen and line. If necessary, remove and clean carburetor.
Tank cap vent obstructed	Open vent in fuel tank cap, or replace cap.
Water in fuel	Drain tank. Clean carburetor and fuel lines. Dry spark plug points. Fill tank with clean, fresh fuel.
Engine over-choked	Close fuel shut-off and pull starter until engine starts. Reopen fuel shut-off for normal fuel flow immediately after engine starts.
Improper carburetor adjustment	Adjust carburetor.
Loose or defective magneto wiring	Check magneto wiring for shorts or grounds; repair if necessary.
Faulty magneto	Check timing and, if necessary, overhaul magneto.
Spark plug fouled	Clean and regap spark plug.
Spark plug porcelain cracked	Replace spark plug.
Poor compression	Overhaul engine.
ENGINE KNOCKS	
Carbon in combustion chamber	Remove cylinder head or cylinder and clean carbon from head and piston.
Loose or worn connecting rod	Replace connecting rod.
Loose flywheel	Check flywheel key and keyway; replace parts if necessary. Tighten flywheel nut to proper torque.
Worn cylinder	Replace cylinder.
Improper magneto timing	Time magneto.

Cause	Remedy
ENGINE MISSES UNDER LOAD	
Spark plug fouled	Clean and regap spark plug.
Spark plug porcelain cracked	Replace spark plug.
Improper spark plug gap	Regap spark plug.
Pitted magneto breaker points	Clean and dress breaker points. Replace badly pitted breaker points.
Magneto breaker arm sluggish	Clean and lubricate breaker point arm.
Faulty condenser (except on Tecumseh Magneto)	Check condenser on a tester; replace if defective (see test instrument instructions and specifications).
Improper carburetor adjustment	Adjust carburetor.
Reed fouled or sluggish	Clean or replace reed.
Crankcase seals leak	Replace worn crankcase seals. Some engines have no lower seal. Check bearing surface of bottom half of crankcase.
ENGINE LACKS POWER	
Choke partially closed	Open choke.
Improper carburetor adjustment	Adjust carburetor.
Magneto improperly timed	Time magneto.
Worn piston or rings	Replace piston or rings.
Air cleaner fouled	Clean air cleaner.
Reed fouled or sluggish	Clean or replace reed.
Improper amount of oil in fuel mixture	Drain tank; fill with correct mixture (See engine decal).
Crankcase seals leaking	Replace worn crankcase seals. Some engines have no lower seal. Check bearing surface of crankshaft.
ENGINE OVERHEATS	
Engine improperly timed	Time engine.
Carburetor improperly adjusted	Adjust carburetor.

Cause	Remedy
ENGINE OVERHEATS (Cont.)	
Air flow obstructed	Remove any obstructions from air passages in shrouds.
Cooling fins clogged	Clean cooling fins.
Excessive load on engine	Check operation of driven equipment. Reduce excessive load.
Carbon in combustion chamber	Remove cylinder head or cylinder and clean carbon from head and piston.
Improper amount of oil in fuel mixture	Drain tank; fill with correct mixture.
ENGINE SURGES OR RUNS UNEVENLY	
Fuel tank cap vent hole clogged	Open vent hole.
Governor parts sticking or binding	Clean, and if necessary repair governor parts.
Carburetor throttle linkage or throttle shaft and/or butterfly binding or sticking	Clean, lubricate, or adjust linkage and de-burr throttle shaft or butterfly.
ENGINE VIBRATES EXCESSIVELY	
Engine not securely mounted	Tighten loose mounting bolts. (See equipment instructions).
Bent crankshaft	Replace crankshaft.
Driven equipment out of balance	Recheck driven equipment.

Cam gear and crankshaft align according to timing marks in Briggs engines.

A view of crankshaft and cam gear, Briggs engine

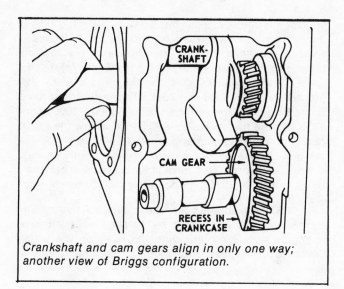

Crankshaft and cam gears align in only one way; another view of Briggs configuration.

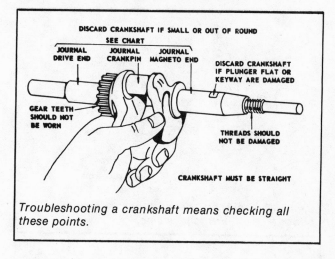

DISCARD CRANKSHAFT IF SMALL OR OUT OF ROUND
SEE CHART

JOURNAL DRIVE END JOURNAL CRANKPIN JOURNAL MAGNETO END

DISCARD CRANKSHAFT IF PLUNGER FLAT OR KEYWAY ARE DAMAGED

GEAR TEETH SHOULD NOT BE WORN

THREADS SHOULD NOT BE DAMAGED

CRANKSHAFT MUST BE STRAIGHT

Troubleshooting a crankshaft means checking all these points.

more than .008 with one .015 gasket, a thrust washer can be placed on the crankshaft power take-off end, between the gear and the crankcase cover. Then you will need to add additional gaskets of .005 or .009 to the .015 inch gasket. In these small Briggs engines it is necessary to start with not less than the .015 inch gasket. To check end play you can either use a dial indicator — a nice gadget to own, by the way — or a feeler gauge. But the feeler gauge can only be used if you back the end of the crankshaft up against something that doesn't move and check it that way or — this is the way the professionals do it — install some kind of pulley or wheel on the end of the crankshaft and up against the sump, then use the feeler gauge between the sump and the pulley. Rather frustrating.

As to ball bearings, in those models that do not use the plain bearing, you may wonder about their condition. But unless the crankshaft is loose, or the bearing makes noise, or you can feel vibration at that power end when the blade is removed and the engine is running, let

CRANKSHAFT REJECT SIZES

BASIC MODEL SERIES	P.T.O. JOURNAL	MAG. JOURNAL	CRANKPIN
ALUMINUM CYLINDER			
6B, 60000	.8726	.8726	.8697
8B, 80000	.8726	.8726	.9963
82000, 92000	.8726	.8726	.9963
100000, 130000	.9976	.8726	.9963
140000, 170000	1.1790	.9975#	1.090
190000	1.1790	.9975#	1.1219
CAST IRON CYLINDER			
5, 6, 8, N	.8726	.8726	.7433
9	.9832	.9832	.8726
14, 19, 190000	1.1790	1.1790	.9964
200000	1.1790	1.1790	1.1219
23, 230000	1.3759	1.3759	1.1844
240000	Ball	Ball	1.3094
300000, 320000	Ball	Ball	1.3094

CHECKING CAM GEAR

BASIC MODEL SERIES	CAM GEAR OR SHAFT JOURNALS	CAM LOBE
ALUMINUM CYLINDER		
6B, 60000	.4985	.883
8B, 80000	.4985	.883
82000, 92000	.4985	.883
100000, 130000	.4985	.950
140000, 170000, 190000	.4985	.977
CAST IRON CYLINDER		
5, 6, 8, N	.3719	.875
9	.3719	1.124
14, 19, 190000	.4968	1.115
200000	.4968	1.115
23, 230000	.4968	1.184
240000	.4968	1.184
300000	#	1.184
320000	#	1.215

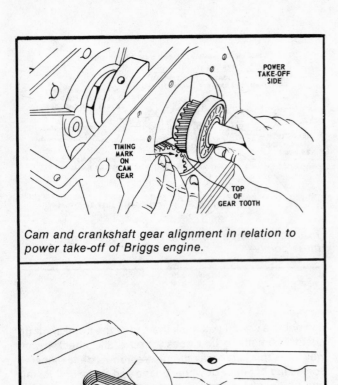

Cam and crankshaft gear alignment in relation to power take-off of Briggs engine.

Measuring end play on Briggs engine.

brate at this point), you can buy a new seal, dig the old one out with a screwdriver and push the new one in. It goes in, sharp edge of the leather or rubber toward the inside of the engine. Put "Lubriplate" on the inside diameter of the oil seal before you install it. Lubriplate is a white, soft grease. As you can see, the seal is flush with the surface. Some Briggs engines (models 60000, 80000, 100000 and 130000) have the seal pressed 3/6-inch below the crankcase mounting flange (surface). As to the bearing (cylinder, actually, that the crankshaft turns in), there's little you can do if it's worn. You'll have to have it reamed out and a bushing installed to fit. It's definitely a machine shop operation.

Clinton engine bearings are tapered, ball, needle and sleeve types. They are to be investigated only if there is engine vibration that cannot be fixed on the blade. Clinton bearings, like Briggs, do not lend themselves to

sleeping bearings lie. But if it is defective, it must be pressed off, or pounded off. To put the new one on is tricky and goes like this: heat the bearing in a pan of engine oil over the stove, but suspend the bearing on something—a bolt or piece of wood, or whatever so that the bearing isn't touching the heated surface. The oil shouldn't be heated over 325 degrees, but that's boiling in oil which one doesn't usually wish on so friendly an entity as a bearing. When the bearing is well done, pour out the oil, take the bearing with a heavy asbestos pad, (or something) and with the bearing shield down, push it on the crankshaft. It will slip on and if it takes a bit of coaxing it won't be much —a slight tapping with a wood block against it and a soft hammer. Let it cool and it will tighten.

For most small Briggs engines, when the plain bearing in the sump is worn—it leaks, is loose and causes vibration—the cure is a new sump. There is no cure for the bearing, since it is in effect merely a machined surface, which is no bearing at all. There is no cure for nothing, excepting, in this case, a new sump.

As to the bearing at the magneto, here too you deal with a cylinder and an oil seal. If it's only the oil seal that's leaking (and the crankshaft doesn't wobble or vi-

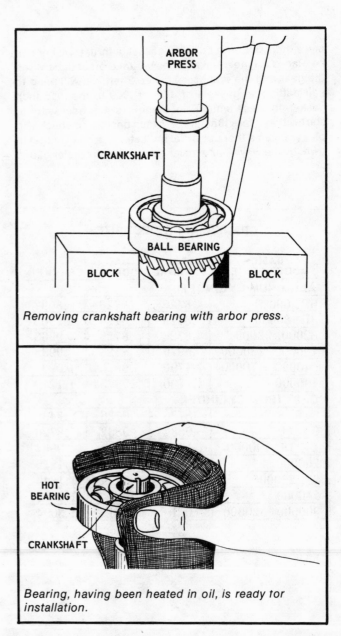

Removing crankshaft bearing with arbor press.

Bearing, having been heated in oil, is ready for installation.

simple replacement, like one can of beans for another, and unless you are expert in the matter of bearings — if you have had automobile bearing experience, for example — it is best to give them a wide berth. But lawn mower engine bearings rarely burn out, so take cheer, at least on this score. However, sleeve bearings can be replaced by you fairly easily. A sleeve bearing, in either Clinton or Briggs engines, is simply a machined cylindrical surface into which the crankshaft fits without play and is anchored there, to turn. If this surface wears, as is inevitable, you can drive out the old bushing — provided you support the plate surface you are banging on, otherwise you'll wind up buying a new engine — and drive in the new. The driving out needn't be too meticulous — that is, so long as the

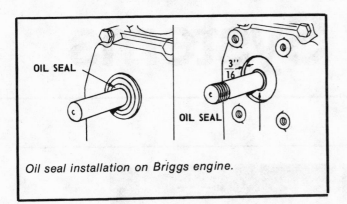

Oil seal installation on Briggs engine.

surface is supported you can bang away at it with whatever tool will fit. But the driving in must be careful, so as not to ruin the bushing. Use a piece of wood against the new bushing.

Oil leakage, which is treacherous and elusive at best, can also be caused by a failure of the breather valve. If you look at the sort-of oblong plate, not far from the muffler, held in place by two screws at opposite ends, you will have located the little monster — its cover, that is. (It isn't in the same place on all Briggs engines or Clintons either, but it's there, in some form.) The breather helps keep vacuum in the crankcase. It has a fiber valve which, when the piston moves back and forth, limits the direction of air flow — air can flow out, but the one-way valve prevents it from flowing in, thus saving the vacuum. If the vacuum fails — i.e., the valve lets air back in — oil will be forced out of the engine, through gaskets, seals, rings, wherever it can.

If you're having oil leak troubles of a general, but baffling nature, remove the breather plate, and take a spark plug wire gauge (a feeler gauge with right-angled wires of various tolerances) and test the breather assembly. Push the .045-inch feeler wire into the fiber disc valve — the space between the valve and the body of the assembly. But don't apply force. If the .045 feeler gauge wire can enter that space you need a new one. Some breather valves are vented from the outside plate with a tube and others are vented inside or rather through the air cleaner, as one of the two tubes going into the carburetor assembly (This is the most common form of venting.)

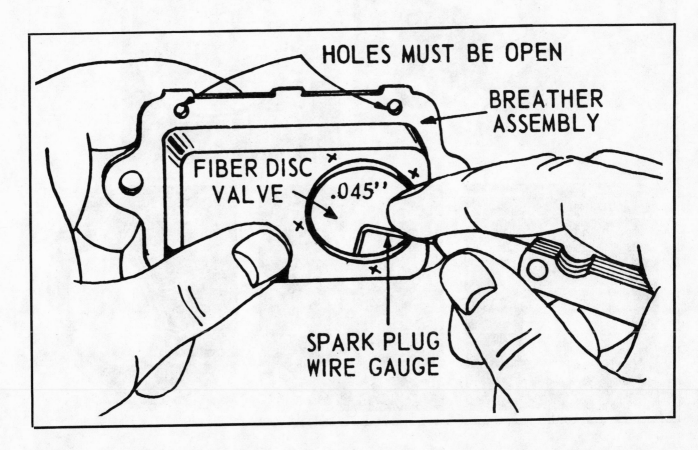

Chapter Three

Accessory Systems

STARTERS

The most common method of starting small mower engines is the rope and pulley method. To replace the rope when, inevitably, it wears out you first push it through the handle and knot it with your Sunday best knot. If you don't own one, make a figure eight knot, then put a pin through the knot and pull it tightly into the handle. You need a rope inserter tool to complete the job. This requires a piece of rather stout wire to which you attach the end of the wire. Flatten it, thread wire and rope into the rope eyelet and out the pulley hole — it must pass inside the guide lug, if there is one (not on newer models). When it is through, tie a knot in rope and pull it tightly until the knot is pulled into the pulley hole.

The other member of the rope starter team that sometimes needs replacement is the spring. To do that you remove the rope by cutting the knot at the starter pulley. Then, grab the end of the starter spring with the pliers and pull it out as far as you can. Bend one of the bumper tangs up and lift out the starter pulley. Disconnect the spring. To put a new one in, insert either end into the blower housing slot and hook it into the pulley. Put the pulley into its housing and bend the bumper tang back into place.

The windup starter, with the folding crank handle and either a knob release or a control lever release, can be trouble if you try to take it apart without unwinding the spring. If you can't get it to release by putting the knob or lever to start, put control at the crank position. Then, hold crank handle with one hand while removing the phillips head screw and the handle assembly from the starter housing. That will release the spring.

If you wish to check the starter spring while on the engine — if you aren't sure that the spring is broken — place the control knob or lever on start. Turn the cranking handle ten clockwise turns. Release the starter and if the engine doesn't turn over it's the spring or, possibly, the clutch isn't catching. While turning the cranking handle, watch the starter clutch ratchet, that thing that catches the starting mechanism and prevents the spring from unwinding as you use the crank. If it does not move, this is a sign that the starter spring is broken.

Replacing the spring requires taking off the housing. Remove the screw that holds the crank to the housing. Bend the tangs that hold the starter spring and housing assembly upward. Now lift the retainer plate, spring and housing assembly from the blower housing. Don't tamper with the starter spring — leave it in the housing. Replace the spring and its housing as a unit.

When putting the housing together, put grease on all moving parts, including the ratchet teeth and the control lever or knob. Don't omit the spring washer in the housing before you replace the cup, spring and release assembly. Then, bend down the retaining tangs.

Cutting grass, the nominal point of the lawn mower engine, is accomplished by the blade. That device may have only one function, but it has several diseases of a debilitating nature. In addition to dulling itself, thus failing to perform its primary function, it can also create several forms of mayhem within the working of the engine. If it gets too dull it causes the engine to work harder. That strains the valves, piston, connecting rod, crankshaft and everything else under pressure in the engine, and shortens the engine's life. If the blade gets loose it can shorten yours. It can also set up vibration in the engine, if one side of the blade becomes lopsided. Engine vibration will, sooner or later, wreck the engine. It could also loosen the

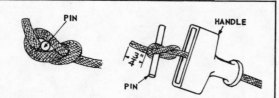

New starter rope is installed with a pin inside the knot. Use figure eight knot; pull tightly into handle.

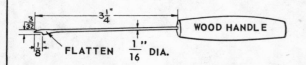

A tool for working with rope starter.

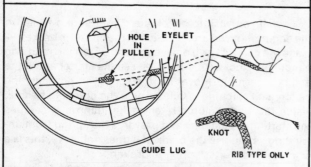

Threading rope through hole in pulley. Rope must pass inside guide lug on some pulleys.

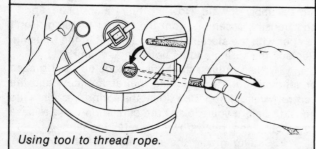

Using tool to thread rope.

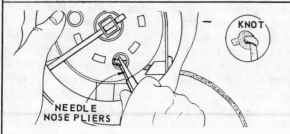

Needle nose pliers help pull rope and knot it.

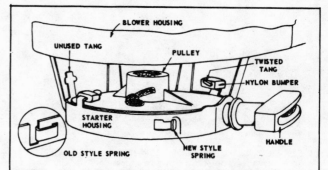

Blower housing, rope and two types of spring catches.

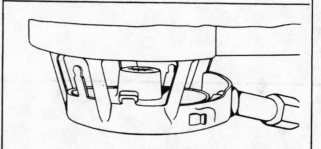

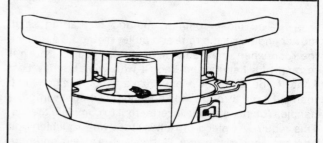

Two styles of Briggs & Stratton blower housings.

To remove spring on Briggs & Stratton housing, grasp and pull out of housing as far as you can. Bend bumper tang up and lift out starter pulley, which disconnects spring.

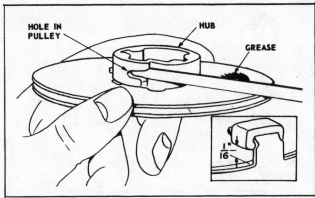

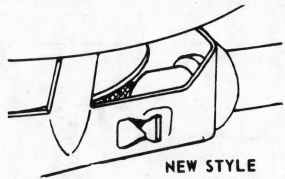

NEW STYLE

Replacing spring: straighten it out to ease installation and restore tension. Either end of spring goes into housing slot and hooks into pulley. It helps to clean spring in solvent, then wipe it by pulling it through cloth. It also helps to put a bit of grease on the pulley. Put pulley in housing and bend bumper tang down. This is the windup starter method. Recoil starters have different, simpler spring configurations.

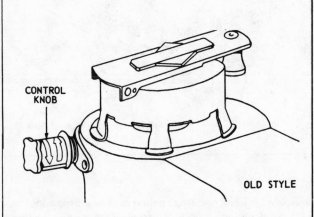

Control knob on Briggs & Stratton windup starter "old style."

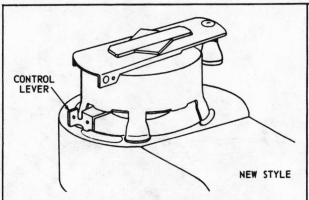

Control lever release on windup starter, typical of recent Briggs & Stratton engines.

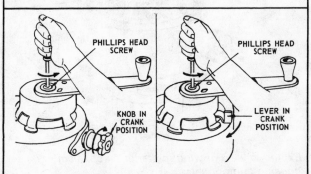

Phillips screw in center of windup starter should be released to remove housing for checking spring.

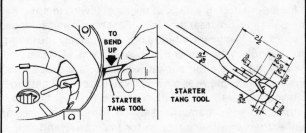

There's a special tang tool made by Briggs & Stratton.

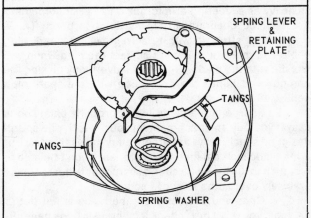

Windup starter components.

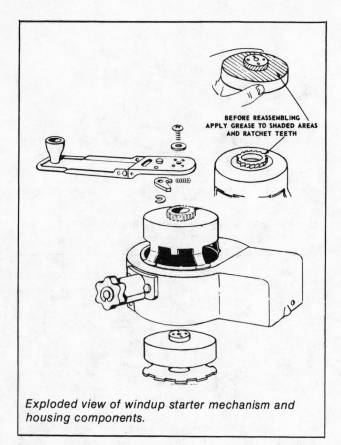

Exploded view of windup starter mechanism and housing components.

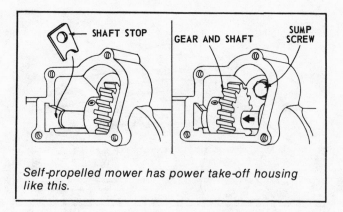

Self-propelled mower has power take-off housing like this.

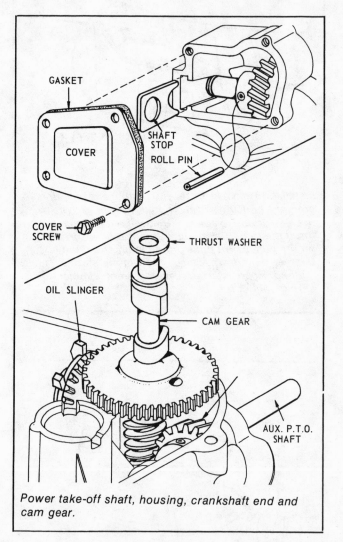

Power take-off shaft, housing, crankshaft end and cam gear.

nuts and/or bolts holding the blade to the engine, freeing it for a devastating whack at the local environment. That includes you. So, treat the blade with caution and science.

To remove the blade requires usually loosening one big bolt in the center of it, heavily torqued. It can only be budged with a big socket wrench or a big open-end wrench, or any big wrench. And if you succeed at getting it off, you must replace it with a wrench that will tighten it ruthlessly — no compromise. The torque must be far higher than any other nut or bolt on the mower, and akin to heavy auto engine torques. Most mower torques are inch pounds; the blade torque is in foot-pounds, and should be as heavy as a steering arm torque on a car or something like that (100 foot-pounds, or in that neighborhood). That's tight. You'll struggle with it, so remove the spark plug cable and make sure it can't contact the plug when you wrestle with the blade. You'll be inadvertently turning the engine over, hence the precaution with the spark plug cable.

Sharpening a blade that is properly balanced is easy if you buy an attachment for your ¼-inch power drill designed specifically to sharpen rotary mower blades. But if the blade isn't balanced, you probably won't be able to restore it to the pink with such a sharpener. It must balance precisely over some kind of fulcrum.

Once you are confident the blade is not out of balance, you must next check it for cracks. Look carefully over the entire surface, then bang on the blade, while you suspend it in one hand. It should be a bright sound, not a dull one. If it has no resonance, but sounds like hitting the

side of a Model T engine, it's time for a new blade. Incidentally, sharpening a good blade doesn't mean sharpening it like a knife. On the contrary, you want an edge that is thin but not knife-like.

Self-propelled devices are either belts or chains driven by the engine and attached to the wheels by means of a system of pulleys and a clutch. The power usually comes from the common vertical crankshaft to which is added a pulley. This pulley gets a belt or chain leading to an axle pulley that turns a wheel. This Rube Goldberg series will pull the mower alright, but it will also play havoc with the innards of the engine, whose power at 3½ horses, it not unlimited. But if you keep the pulleys well oiled and clean, the belt in good condition and the chain, if that's it, oiled, you diminish the strain on the engine. There is one other type, superior to the kind we're talking about. This method gets power from the engine inside and above the blade. It comes off the crankshaft as an auxiliary power take-off shaft, geared into the crankshaft. It is by far the better system; it's substantially designed and engineered, and the gears and bearings involved are much better able to withstand the demands than the externally designed system that takes power directly off the crankshaft above the blade. The shaft of this inside system rotates one revolution for every 8½ turns of the crankshaft. In this system (Briggs models 92580 and 92980), cam gear, worm gear and oil slinger are an assembly not available separately. If one part of the system breaks down you buy the whole system anew.

If you need to inspect the inside gear of this auxiliary power take-off system, on the Briggs models specified, you will see the cover quickly enough. It comes off once you remove the mounting screws. It should last as long as the rest of the engine components. The only trouble might arise from some accident that shears off the gear, or from excessive use without change of oil.

The chain of command, from engine crankshaft to wheels (front or rear — there are both types), may be long and devious with many interlocking devices along the way, or it may consist of only a few components. But all will be similar, allowing for the riotous designers who come up with these things. Trouble can be pinpointed by turning the wheels or blade (the spark plug disconnected, as always), until you find something that doesn't turn, or something that wobbles, catches, grinds or bumps. That's the part you replace, up to and including the entire power take-off assembly of the Briggs engines we're talking about. Clinton engines have the same system.

Starting systems

Among accessory systems that you don't need but that offer convenience and extra cost are the various self-starters. Most riding mowers have them, and so do some self-propelled and simple rotaries. Of course, as engines get over 3.5 h.p. they become harder to turn with a rope, and electric starters achieve respectability as well as utility. They do, as we will see, add enormously to the bag and baggage, the complexity, the fragility and temperament of the engine. And while cranking systems in automobiles seem to go on forever, more or less, many of us have rueful recollections of the starter that wouldn't. Lawn mower engine starters, though as complex as automobile, aren't as rugged.

You start with the battery, a 12-volt, 50-amp, negatively grounded to terminal affair, like the usual car battery which in fact it resembles, though it may be of different shape or size. You have to check and maintain the battery,

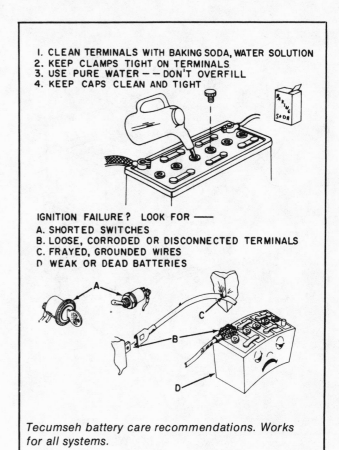

1. CLEAN TERMINALS WITH BAKING SODA, WATER SOLUTION
2. KEEP CLAMPS TIGHT ON TERMINALS
3. USE PURE WATER — — DON'T OVERFILL
4. KEEP CAPS CLEAN AND TIGHT

IGNITION FAILURE? LOOK FOR ——
A. SHORTED SWITCHES
B. LOOSE, CORRODED OR DISCONNECTED TERMINALS
C. FRAYED, GROUNDED WIRES
D. WEAK OR DEAD BATTERIES

Tecumseh battery care recommendations. Works for all systems.

exactly as in your family jalopy; check the water (electrolyte) level every so often (100 hours, the manual says, but every month at least in season), and add distilled water. Warning, don't over-fill. Keep the battery top clean, and wash it with a brush or rag dipped in ammonia or bicarbonate of soda solution, then clean it off with a rag dipped in water. If the hold-down clamps of the battery get loose the case can crack; so will it if you tighten the clamps excessively. Walk that thin line carefully. When corrosion appears at the terminals, remove the cables and brush all the acid away, then put grease or petroleum jelly on the corroded parts, but not on the surfaces that pass electricity. All this is standard advice to any car battery owner; it applies equally to our lawn mower engine.

Lawn mower engine starting systems differ in several ways among themselves. One unit combines the function of the starting motor and the generator (in cars these are always two separate units). Other units have separate starting motors with separate charging units that are not part of the system. Some systems use 110 volt AC motors that are plugged into a house outlet for starting. These, of course, require no chargers. Other systems are exactly like automobiles — starting motor, generator (alternator), regulator and battery.

Drive systems are of two kinds — belt and pulley, and pinion gear starters exactly similar to those of automobile starters. Belt and pulley types are on the starter generator systems.

Starter generator systems (12 volt) have a reg-

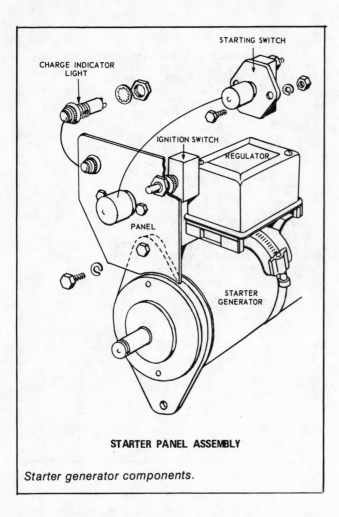

CHARGE INDICATOR LIGHT

STARTING SWITCH

IGNITION SWITCH

REGULATOR

PANEL

STARTER GENERATOR

STARTER PANEL ASSEMBLY

Starter generator components.

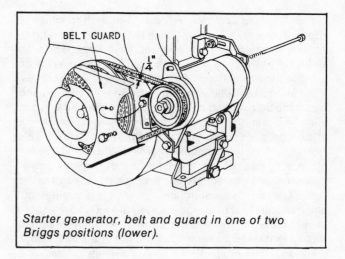

BELT GUARD

1/4"

Starter generator, belt and guard in one of two Briggs positions (lower).

One simple way of increasing the charge rate is to disconnect the lead to the regulator BAT terminal (it's so marked), and connect it to the regulator L terminal. What this does is bypass the current-voltage system of the regulator, and automatically increases the amount of charge. Warning: use this method only in cold weather when operating periods are short or infrequent, and when you resume regular or more extended use of the motor you must restore the original wiring connections. Otherwise, the battery will be over-charged with possible burnout resulting.

Trouble shooting starter generator models involves mostly maintenance of battery and cables. When battery water isn't kept up, or cables become corroded, and battery top is allowed to corrode, starting efficiency is lowered and even stopped entirely. You can usually see when the belt is worn or broken by visual inspection. Failure of any of the switches is rare. When the ammeter or idiot light indicates discharge look first outside the motor — the switches themselves and connections in and out of them, connections to the ammeter and/or light, and connections at the motor, and, of course, at the battery. The starter generator and regulator need special test equipment to examine them. If you clean and tighten all connections and get no results you'll need to have the starter generator and regulator tested. Remove the unit from the engine and take it to a dealer where you can expect to pay very little for the testing.

Starter motors with drive gears are both 12 volt DC and 110 volt AC. The gears are exactly similar to automobile starting gears. When the starter is turned on the helix on the motor shaft drives the pinion gear into the ring gear on the engine flywheel, thus cranking the engine. With the 110 volt AC power source, which must be plugged into such an outlet during starting, there is also a rectifier to convert the AC current into 12 volt DC. Otherwise, operation of the motor itself is the same. Wiring, of course, is altogether different; so is the switching, and the charging.

Gear drive starter systems break down potentially every step of the way. The flywheel ring gear, for example, into which the starter pinion gear is driven (for cranking),

ulator strapped on them which controls charging voltage into the battery. Three types of wirings are found on starter generator (12 volt) systems. One type has a solenoid and key starter with an ammeter to indicate charge or discharge. Another type has a manual start switch (but no solenoid coil). The third type has a starter panel with a charge indicator light, a manual start switch, and an ignition switch — one extra switch to turn. In all cases the battery is 12 volt, 40 to 45 amps minimum capacity.

Starter generator systems start the engine by means of a belt-driven pulley on both motor and engine. If the belt needs replacement you need to remove the belt guard. Then loosen the unit mounting bolts enough to push the motor towards the engine as far as you can. Now remove the belt (some of these units require two belts). Check the belt for wear, glaze, breaks and tears. If one belt needs replacing replace both. Don't force the belts in or out of pulleys. If force is needed it means you haven't loosened the mounting bolts sufficiently (or pushed the motor far enough towards the engine). Belts are of special material.

Starter generator motors that are used infrequently at low temperatures may not run enough to charge the battery sufficiently. Result? Poor cold weather starting (if the unit is used in snow clearing operations).

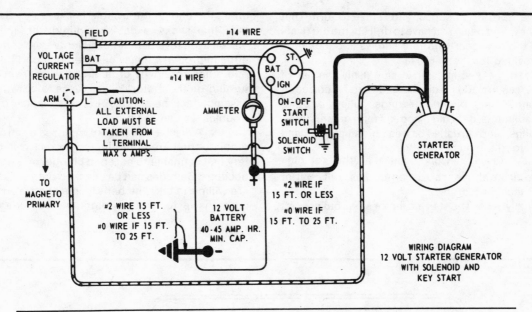

WIRING DIAGRAM
12 VOLT STARTER GENERATOR
WITH SOLENOID AND
KEY START

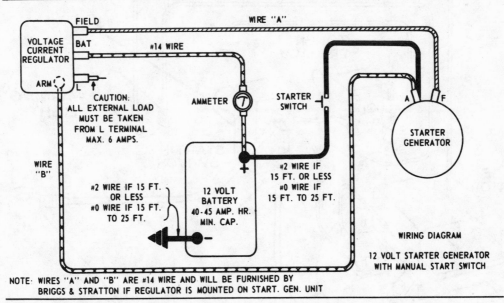

WIRING DIAGRAM

12 VOLT STARTER GENERATOR
WITH MANUAL START SWITCH

NOTE: WIRES "A" AND "B" ARE #14 WIRE AND WILL BE FURNISHED BY
BRIGGS & STRATTON IF REGULATOR IS MOUNTED ON START. GEN. UNIT

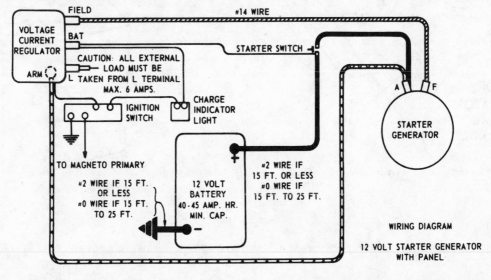

WIRING DIAGRAM

12 VOLT STARTER GENERATOR
WITH PANEL

can become worn or damaged, and refuse to turn. That requires a new ring gear. You have to drill out the old rivets and install the new gear with four screws and lock nuts that are provided for the purpose.

When the engine cranks sluggishly the list of trouble sources includes a discharged battery, corroded or poor connections, binding bearings, pulleys or other power impediments, dirty or corroded motor commutator, worn bearings, worn brushes or weak brush springs and using the wrong oil in cold weather.

But if the engine won't crank at all, the problems can include all the above in acute forms, plus faulty starter switch and faulty motor itself.

Finally, when the starting motor spins but doesn't crank the engine the trouble is caused by a dirty pinion gear that sticks, a damaged pinion or ring gear, and maybe even reversed motor polarity from somebody tinkering improperly. It may be noted that on 110-volt motors one other possibility of failure is there, especially when turning on the motor causes fuses to blow; the rectifier assembly can be shorted. Let's see which of the above troubles we can solve.

A discharged battery is caused by an alternator or regulator that aren't producing correct voltage or a battery that is unable to accept a charge, or poor cable connections. Batteries can be checked out with a tester if you are willing to take the battery to a shop. You can buy an inexpensive tester that might be inaccurate. But first

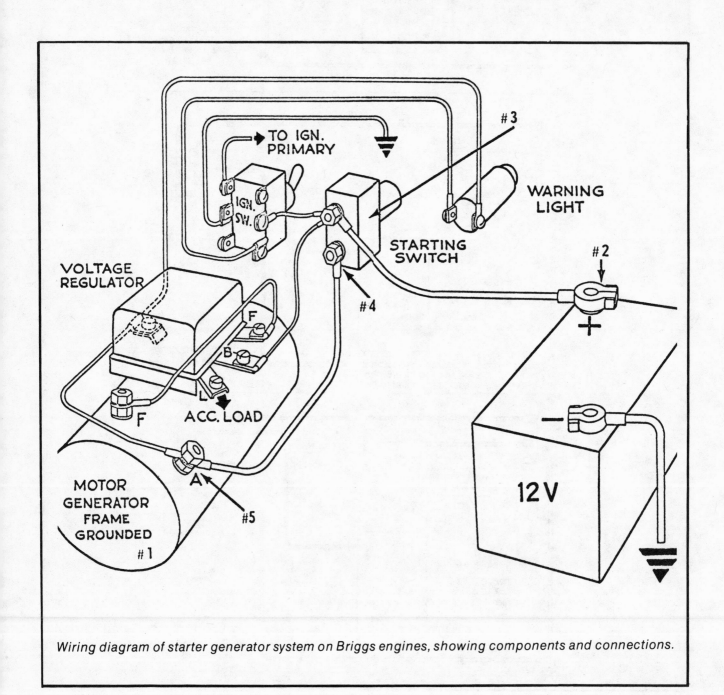

Wiring diagram of starter generator system on Briggs engines, showing components and connections.

check out all the connections in and out of the battery. This cannot be emphasized too strongly; corrosion, dirt and faulty connections cause more electrical troubles than any other single factor.

The starting motor drive assembly is one of the earliest culprits to suspect when the starter clicks on but refuses to turn the engine, or when the motor whirrs around and the engine doesn't crank. You can see this failure by removing the starter shield and turning on the starter. The drive should rise and engage the flywheel ring gear, then turn the engine. If this sequence does not happen it is probable that the gears (helix and pinion) need cleaning and/or replacing. If cleaning doesn't free the starter drive you must replace the complete drive assembly since individual parts are not available.

To remove the starter drive assembly you need to get the lock nut off the end of the drive shaft. This requires some way of holding the pinion gear while you turn the

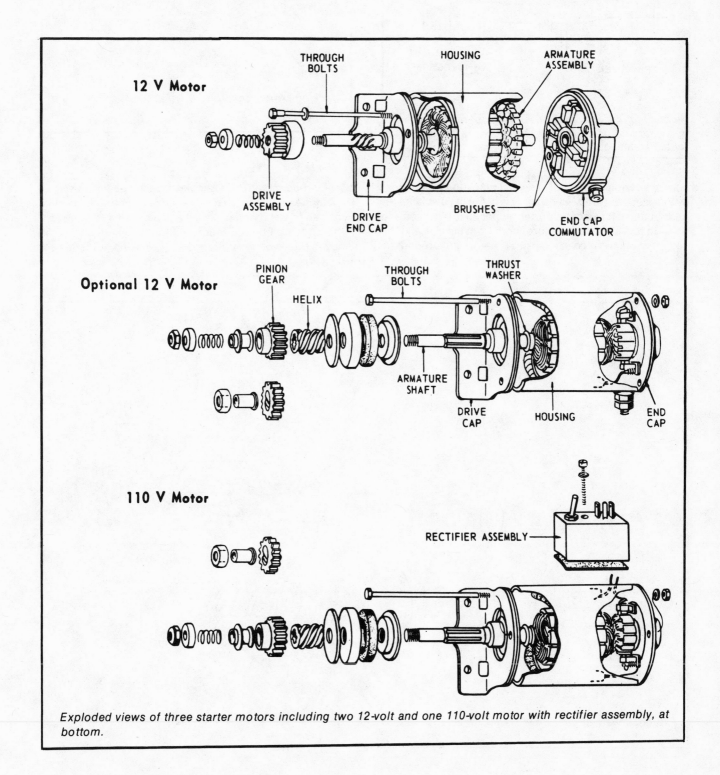

Exploded views of three starter motors including two 12-volt and one 110-volt motor with rectifier assembly, at bottom.

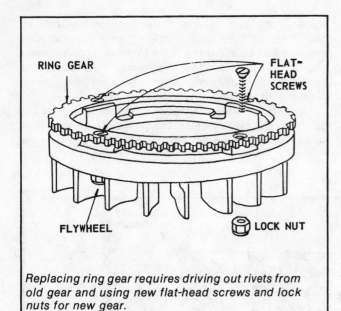

Replacing ring gear requires driving out rivets from old gear and using new flat-head screws and lock nuts for new gear.

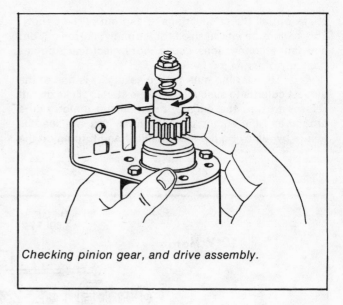

Checking pinion gear, and drive assembly.

socket wrench on the nut. You can block the pinion gear with a piece of wood or you can use a vise. If you clamp the gear in a vise it has to be protected because it isn't strong enough to withstand pressures both from the vise and the socket wrench. You can wrap heavy cardboard around the gear or heavy cloth. If, after cleaning the gear with appropriate cleaner — say Gunk — and it continues to stick you can forget trying to save it and merely try to remove it. This shouldn't be too tough — that is, the nut can be removed once you take off the kid gloves and hold the gear

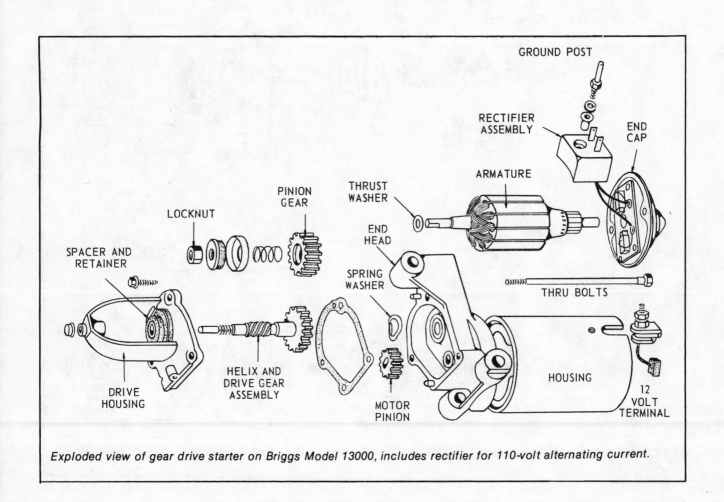

Exploded view of gear drive starter on Briggs Model 13000, includes rectifier for 110-volt alternating current.

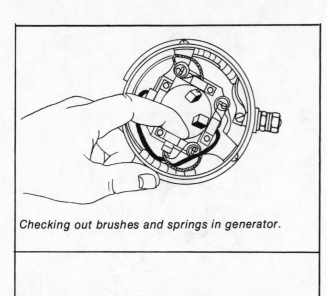

Checking out brushes and springs in generator.

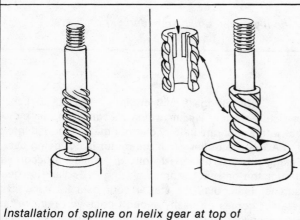

Installation of spline on helix gear at top of crankshaft.

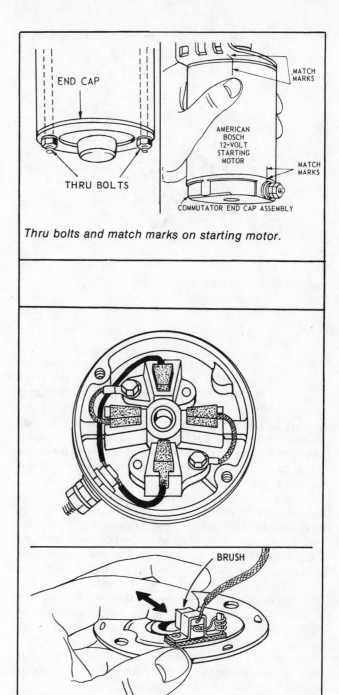

Thru bolts and match marks on starting motor.

Brushes must move freely or springs must be replaced, holder cleaned out.

in whatever device works.

When re-assembly time arrives, you may notice that inside the shaft screw there is a machined spline and this must face upward to the end of the armature shaft. Tighten the nut as it was before. It's a good rule of thumb to remember how much force a nut or bolt requires to get off so that a roughly equal amount can be applied to put it back, if you don't own a torque wrench. The world got to its present state without torque wrenches over large parts of it, and the torque wrench didn't make its appearance in force in our society until very recent times, so while it is now indispensable in many higher types of machines the lawn mower engine doesn't really qualify in that category.

If your starter isn't fixed by the job just completed — the sticking pinion gear — that means it has internal problems. The most common of them is defective brushes.

If inspection shows that the motor needs new brushes, that too is easy enough. But you do have to get at the brushes. Before taking the motor apart, turn it carefully by hand and listen for bearing noise or feel it for bearing binding. There should be neither noise nor bind-

ing of the motor. If turning by hand produces a suspicious sound that indicates bearing problems, and you can feel it binding, the problem is not merely brushes, though these too probably will be worn.

To get at the brushes and commutator requires removing the thru-bolts, washers and end cap. Thru-bolts and nuts must go back on the same side as originally, otherwise there is the possibility of distortion. So mark

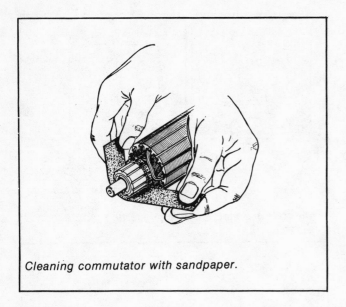

Cleaning commutator with sandpaper.

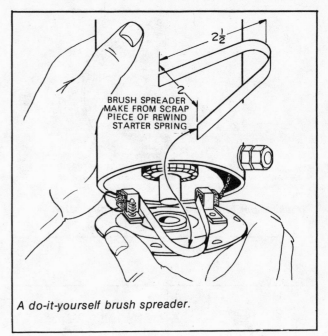

A do-it-yourself brush spreader.

them. Once the nuts and bolts are off, the armature, cap and gear drive will come off. You can look at the commutator. If dirty or worn, it will need "turning" (grinding down) or replacing the armature. To get at it, remove the springs that hold the brushes in place against the commutator and remove the brushes. If you are working on a 110-volt AC starter you will have to unsolder the leads going to the rectifier (and ending at the brushes), if you replace the brushes.

The commutator, even if it doesn't need turning, undoubtedly needs cleaning. Use sandpaper (but not emery cloth, which will ruin new brushes quickly) on the commutator, until it is bright and shiny. Clean all dirt from the end cap, from the armature, and wherever else it accumulates. Then put oil on the end cap bearing surfaces and put new brushes and springs into their holders. Replacing brushes can be slippery business. Some method of holding the brushes in while you get the commutator back in place must be improvised. An extra pair of hands will do it; several small screwdrivers will work, also. When sliding the armature into its housing, you need to match the end cap housing to marks on the housing. The end cap must be returned as it was originally.

Note: 110-volt motors are especially crucial in the matter of matching cap to original position. Also, leads from rectifier which must be re-soldered at the rectifier end, must go back on to the brush holders in the same way they came off. In some models the leads are attached to the brushes and are not detachable.

Starting motors on larger model engines look more or less exactly like automobile starters and behave (or misbehave) in the same ways. Gear drive starters on Briggs models 300400 and 320400, which require a 32-amp battery for ordinary use and a 50-amp battery for zero weather, come apart like the motors we've discussed. Disassembly requires removal of the lock nut and washer, followed by the other components — pinion gear, helix, spring, and the drive cap (if you need to take the motor apart as above for brush and bearing service).

The Briggs 92000 engines may use a nickel-cadmium starting system, which is a smaller starter motor but with a separate battery charger that is plugged into a 110 AC house outlet when the motor is not being used. Taking the starter apart follows similar procedures, though the lock-nut feature is missing. In its place is a gear retainer that holds the starter spur gear in place. The retainer comes off easily enough once you remove the starter cover. On these starters the spur gear is made of nylon and unless it moves freely on the helix gear the starter will not work. If the motor spins but does not start the engine — does not engage the flywheel — remove the

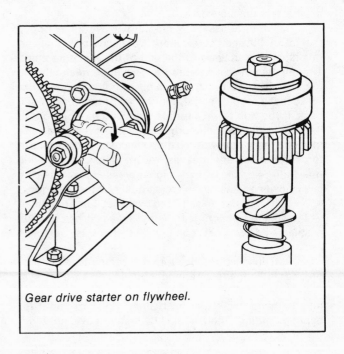

Gear drive starter on flywheel.

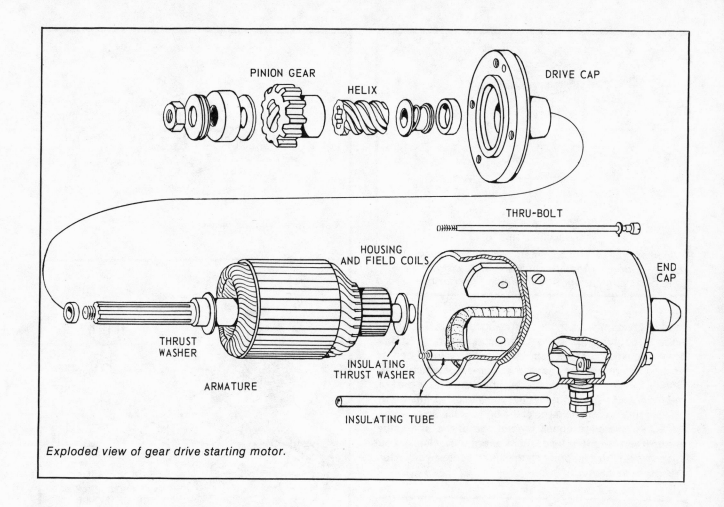

PINION GEAR   HELIX   DRIVE CAP

THRU-BOLT

HOUSING
AND FIELD COILS

END CAP

THRUST
WASHER

INSULATING
THRUST WASHER

ARMATURE

INSULATING TUBE

Exploded view of gear drive starting motor.

starter cover, turn on the starter and watch the results. If the spur gear does not shoot up on the helix gear to force engagement of the flywheel, the spur gear must be cleaned out. If cleaning doesn't solve the problem, replace the unit.

As to the motor end of the nickel-cadmium starter, disassembly follows similar procedures to those we've discussed. The starter cover comes off to inspect helix and nylon spur gear, as noted. Remove the gear retainer and spur gear. Three screws hold the gear cover; once these are out the gear cover itself comes off. Clutch assembly and pinion gear come off. Next, remove starting motor thru-bolts. Take off the motor support cover from the motor shell. The armature is now free to come out the bottom of the shell. Slide the rubber mounted terminal out of the shell with the end cap.

Check the brushes. If they are worn and are less than 1/4 inch in length they must be replaced. Replace springs, also. Clean dirt away from all parts and use sandpaper on the commutator. Clean bearings out and oil them before replacing the motor. When replacing brushes it is always a ticklish problem to keep the brushes in their holders sufficiently to allow the commutator past them. One remedy is to bend a springy piece of metal and force it between the sets of brushes as you manipulate the commutator past the edge of the brushes.

Alternators on those small engines that have

complete starting-generating systems are not fit subjects for home repair. They require special test equipment — a multimeter, such as an Eico Testor No. 540 — which is not worth buying for one session. In any case, alternators are long-suffering beasts of burden, despite their delicate components (diodes), and when your system fails to charge it isn't likely that the alternator is the problem. As we've stressed, the problem is most likely to be in connections between the various links in the cranking system. If

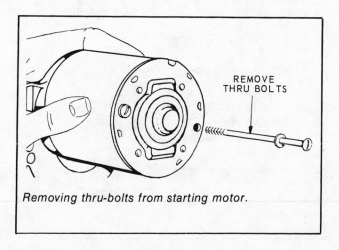

REMOVE
THRU BOLTS

Removing thru-bolts from starting motor.

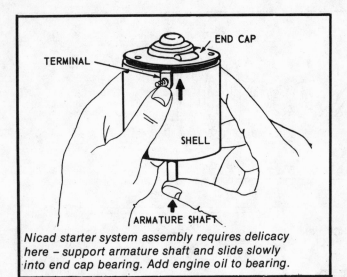

Nicad starter system assembly requires delicacy here – support armature shaft and slide slowly into end cap bearing. Add engine oil to bearing.

the battery continues to discharge, despite good connections throughout the system, (and the battery itself has been checked out), the next investigation should center around the regulator. That too requires test equipment. On the 110 volt AC starter models the regulator is part of the rectifier. Testing requires the use of a DC voltmeter to check the amount of charge at the battery. It also requires an AC voltmeter to check the voltage at the alternator stator (the stationary field of the alternator). Unless you already own this equipment it makes no sense to buy it for this purpose alone.

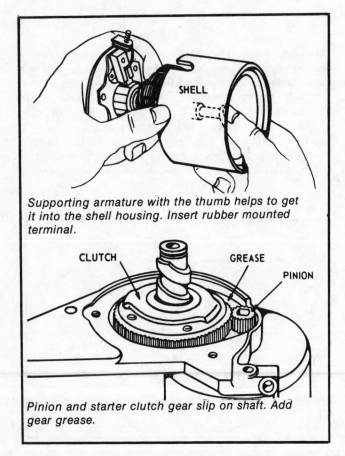

Supporting armature with the thumb helps to get it into the shell housing. Insert rubber mounted terminal.

Pinion and starter clutch gear slip on shaft. Add gear grease.

Make sure brushes move freely.

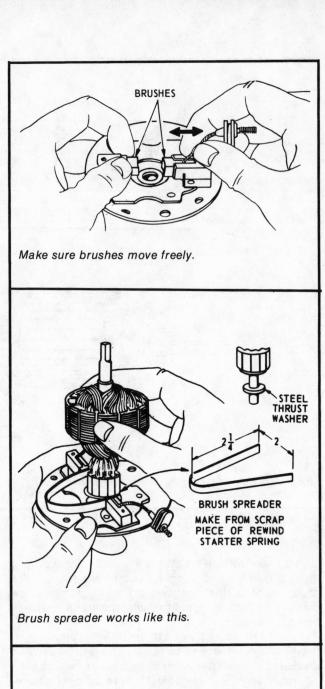

Brush spreader works like this.

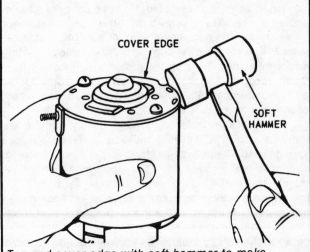

Tap end cover edge with soft hammer to make certain end cap bearing is seated and aligned.

STARTERS
Nicad System

ELECTRIC STARTER KEY SWITCH and WIRING RECOMMENDATIONS
FOR 12 VOLT NICKEL CADMIUM BATTERY STARTING SYSTEM – SERIES 92000 ENGINES

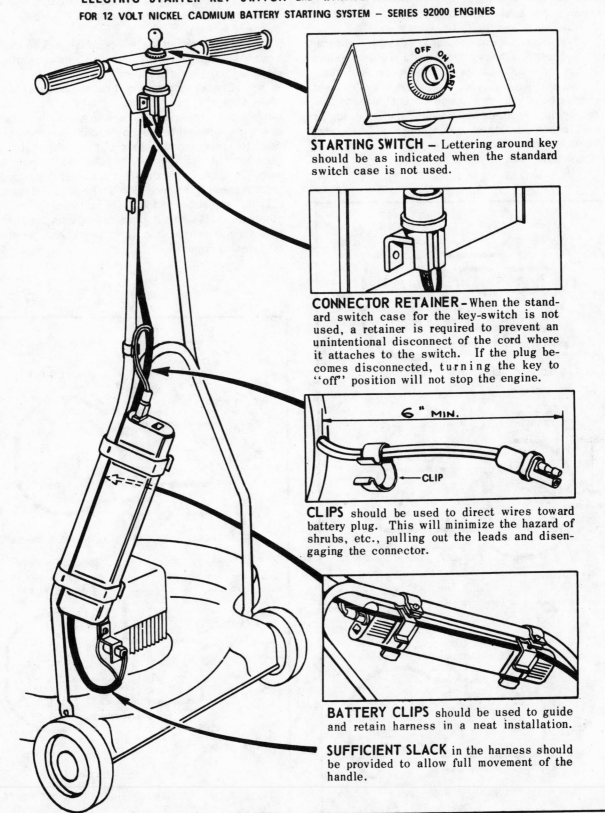

STARTING SWITCH – Lettering around key should be as indicated when the standard switch case is not used.

CONNECTOR RETAINER – When the standard switch case for the key-switch is not used, a retainer is required to prevent an unintentional disconnect of the cord where it attaches to the switch. If the plug becomes disconnected, turning the key to "off" position will not stop the engine.

CLIPS should be used to direct wires toward battery plug. This will minimize the hazard of shrubs, etc., pulling out the leads and disengaging the connector.

BATTERY CLIPS should be used to guide and retain harness in a neat installation.

SUFFICIENT SLACK in the harness should be provided to allow full movement of the handle.

The third principal engine make you will encounter is Tecumseh, which is standard on many different powered devices, including chain saws, boats, snow blowers, tillers, and mowers.

Tecumseh engines, like Briggs & Stratton, and Clinton, come in a variety of configurations of cycle, horsepower, and application. We are mostly interested in the 2-stroke cycle and the 4-stroke cycle.

Tecumseh 2-cycle engines are designed according to the Cross Scavenge principle, which uses a domed piston head; the Loop Scavenge principle, which uses a flat piston head with a vacuum-pressure activated reed valve; and a Loop Scavenge design without the reed valve. These engines are so-named because the Scavenge or exhaust phase eliminates conventional valves, valve springing and valve lifters. It utilizes the reed valve in two cases and eliminates it in the third, replacing the reed valve with an exhaust port. Reed valves are flap or flutter valves opened and shut by crankcase pressure. Reduction of crankcase pressure opens the valve, allowing the fuel-air oil mixture to enter the crankcase. Increased crankcase pressure closes the valve, preventing the fuel-air and oil mixture from escaping back through the carburetor. In the design that eliminates the reed valve, a valve function is performed by a port.

To check out these 2-cycle engines you follow a trouble-shooting pattern somewhat similar to other engines, with these differences.

Check compression: disconnect spark plug, then crank engine by hand in the normal direction, when engine is cold. If there is considerable resistance to turning, as engine approaches the top-dead-center (and you don't need to know exactly where this is; only that there is resistance at one point each cycle, and the point is the same), and the resistance continues on instead of decreasing rapidly, compression is normal. But, if resistance is slight, or resistance decreases rapidly at the peak of it, compression is weak. If you suspect weak compression, take the engine to a place where it can be checked with a compression tester.

FLAT PISTON HEAD

DIRECTION OF ROTATION

REED VALVE

FUEL-AIR MIXTURE

EXHAUST PORTS

LOOP SCAVENGE WITH REED VALVE

DIRECTION OF ROTATION

CARBURETOR

INTAKE PORTS

FUEL-AIR MIXTURE

EXHAUST PORTS

DOMED PISTON HEAD

REED VALVE CLOSED

CROSS SCAVENGE WITH REED VALVE

FLAT PISTON HEAD

AIR

EXHAUST PORTS

FUEL-AIR MIXTURE

LOOP SCAVENGE WITH 3RD PORT

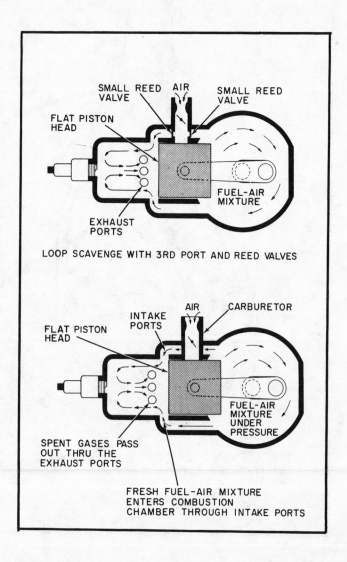

SMALL REED VALVE

AIR

SMALL REED VALVE

FLAT PISTON HEAD

FUEL-AIR MIXTURE

EXHAUST PORTS

LOOP SCAVENGE WITH 3RD PORT AND REED VALVES

INTAKE PORTS

AIR

CARBURETOR

FLAT PISTON HEAD

FUEL-AIR MIXTURE UNDER PRESSURE

SPENT GASES PASS OUT THRU THE EXHAUST PORTS

FRESH FUEL-AIR MIXTURE ENTERS COMBUSTION CHAMBER THROUGH INTAKE PORTS

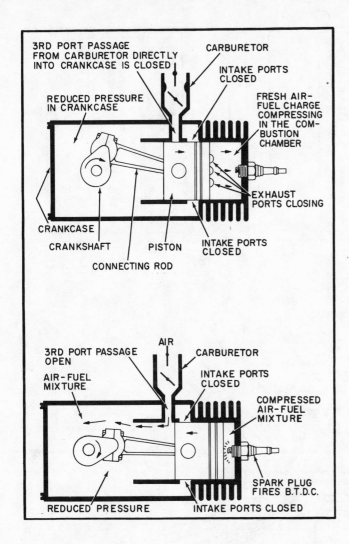

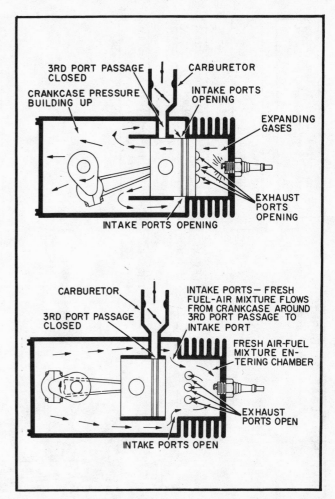

Next, crank engine slowly, listening carefully for scraping or binding noise. Such noises can be caused by bearings, crankshaft or connecting rod. Rock the crankshaft back and forth; if there is much play, suspect worn rod bearings or piston pin.

Check oil seals at the ends of the crankcase. Leaking crankcase seals in the 2-cycle engines will cause faulty fuel metering, hard starting and peculiar, unpredictable operation of the engine. Check everywhere for leaks that are indicated by oil deposits.

Service on any of the engine components follows earlier instructions, allowing for the absence of the valve train system. Reed valves normally require no service, though the ports require cleaning.

Carburetors on Tecumseh engines are both float and pressure differential, as with Briggs, Clinton and other small engines. Their illnesses are the same; so are their repairs. The exception is the power chain carburetor, which must be able to function at any angle. That will be discussed later.

In some Tecumseh carburetors there are two features in regular servicing that can cause trouble. The inlet needle fits in a Viton rubber seat which in turn fits into a brass bowl. When replacing the needle you must replace the seat. Needle replacement is indicated when the needle tip shows any sign of wear. To remove the Viton rubber seat, which is in the carburetor body, put a few drops of heavy engine oil on the seat. Then pry it out with a short piece of hooked wire. When replacing, insert the seat grooved side first. Put a little oil in the cavity and push the seat into position with some flat tool.

The second service item that can make trouble is the welch plug, found on various carburetor models. It's usually removed when cleaning the carburetor. It's a small plug in the body of the carburetor that has a raised surface. To remove it requires a small, pointed chisel. Drive the tip into the plug and pry it out, taking care not to hit anything else in the process. If you don't have a small chisel, take a flat surface tool of some sort and drive it into the raised center of the plug. This will force the plug away from the carburetor body and it will fall out. Clean the area, then put the new plug into its receptacle, with raised portion (convex) up. Force the plug into the receptacle by using a surface equal to or larger than the surface of the plug. Drive the plug in and flatten it in the process. Do not dent the plug or drive the center of it below the top surface of the carburetor. Replace welch plugs only when the carburetor has heavy dirt deposits. See page 70.

Tecumseh has listed a chart of various points to check for carburetor malfunction. It is useful as a general guide to carburetor malfunction. Here it is:

SERVICE HINTS FOR FLOAT CARBURETORS

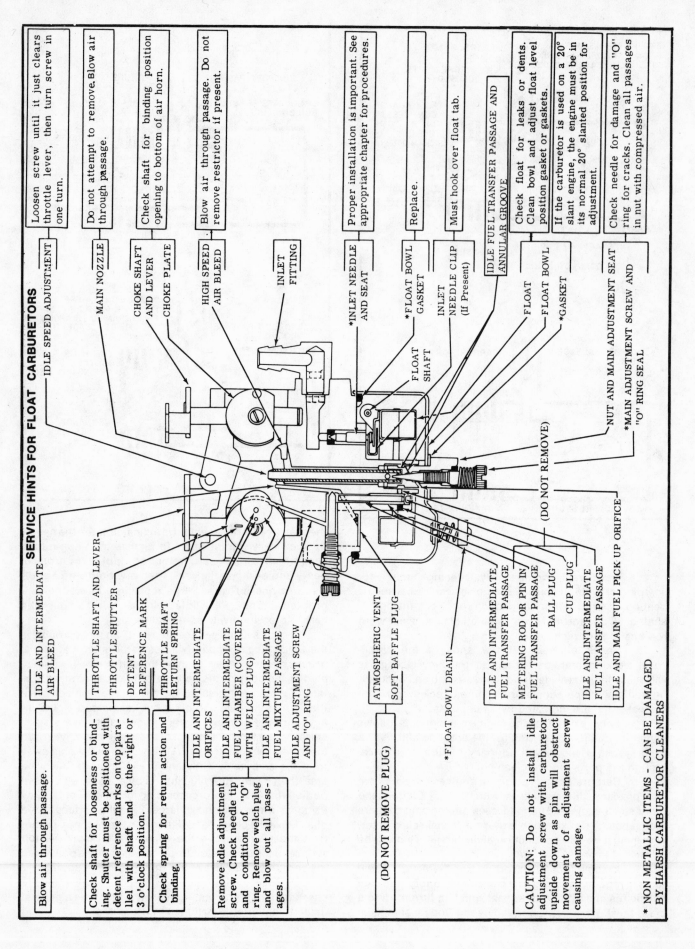

Blow air through passage.

IDLE AND INTERMEDIATE AIR BLEED

Loosen screw until it just clears throttle lever, then turn screw in one turn.

IDLE SPEED ADJUSTMENT

Do not attempt to remove.Blow air through passage.

MAIN NOZZLE

Check shaft for binding position opening to bottom of air horn.

CHOKE SHAFT AND LEVER

CHOKE PLATE

Blow air through passage. Do not remove restrictor if present.

HIGH SPEED AIR BLEED

INLET FITTING

Proper installation is important. See appropriate chapter for procedures.

*INLET NEEDLE AND SEAT

Replace.

*FLOAT BOWL GASKET

Must hook over float tab.

INLET NEEDLE CLIP (If Present)

IDLE FUEL TRANSFER PASSAGE AND ANNULAR GROOVE

Check float for leaks or dents. Clean bowl and adjust float level position gasket or gaskets.

FLOAT

FLOAT BOWL

If the carburetor is used on a 20° slant engine, the engine must be in its normal 20° slanted position for adjustment.

*GASKET

Check needle for damage and "O" ring for cracks. Clean all passages in nut with compressed air.

NUT AND MAIN ADJUSTMENT SEAT

*MAIN ADJUSTMENT SCREW AND "O" RING SEAL

FLOAT SHAFT

Check shaft for looseness or binding. Shutter must be positioned with detent reference marks on top parallel with shaft and to the right or 3 o'clock position.

THROTTLE SHAFT AND LEVER

THROTTLE SHUTTER

DETENT REFERENCE MARK

Check spring for return action and binding.

THROTTLE SHAFT RETURN SPRING

IDLE AND INTERMEDIATE ORIFICES

Remove idle adjustment screw. Check needle tip and condition of "O" ring. Remove welch plug and blow out all passages.

IDLE AND INTERMEDIATE FUEL CHAMBER (COVERED WITH WELCH PLUG)

IDLE AND INTERMEDIATE FUEL MIXTURE PASSAGE

*IDLE ADJUSTMENT SCREW AND "O" RING

ATMOSPHERIC VENT

SOFT BAFFLE PLUG

(DO NOT REMOVE PLUG)

*FLOAT BOWL DRAIN

IDLE AND INTERMEDIATE FUEL TRANSFER PASSAGE

METERING ROD OR PIN IN FUEL TRANSFER PASSAGE

BALL PLUG

CUP PLUG

(DO NOT REMOVE)

IDLE AND INTERMEDIATE FUEL TRANSFER PASSAGE

IDLE AND MAIN FUEL PICK UP ORIFICE

CAUTION: Do not install idle adjustment screw with carburetor upside down as pin will obstruct movement of adjustment screw causing damage.

* NON METALLIC ITEMS - CAN BE DAMAGED BY HARSH CARBURETOR CLEANERS

SERVICE HINTS FOR DIAPHRAGM CARBURETORS

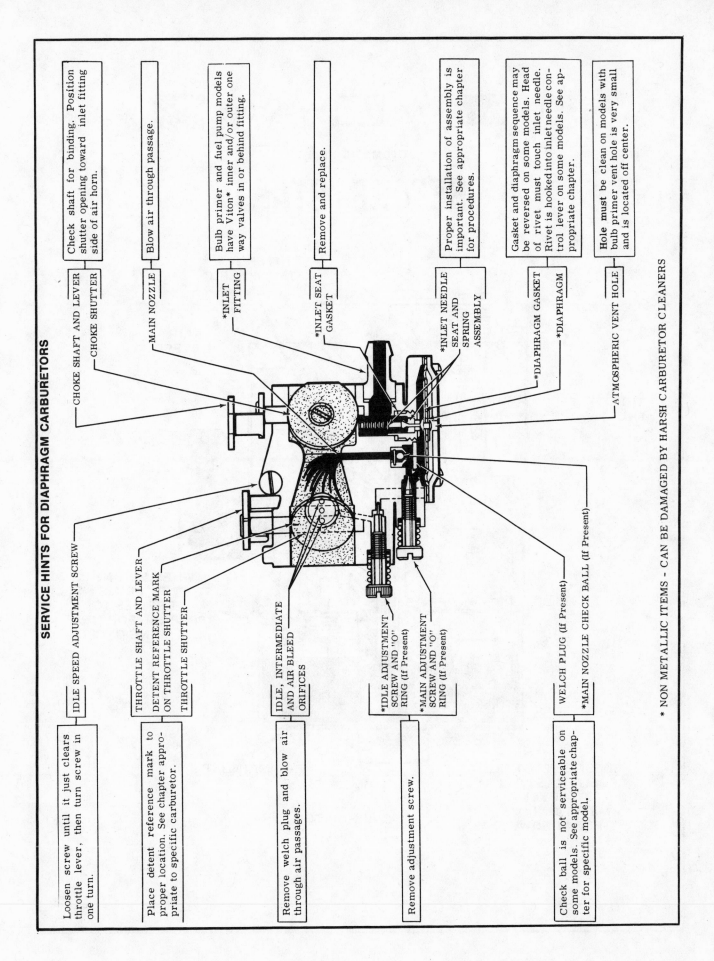

CHOKE SHAFT AND LEVER — Check shaft for binding. Position shutter opening toward inlet fitting side of air horn.

CHOKE SHUTTER

MAIN NOZZLE — Blow air through passage.

INLET FITTING — Bulb primer and fuel pump models have Viton inner and/or outer one way valves in or behind fitting.

*INLET SEAT GASKET — Remove and replace.

*INLET NEEDLE SEAT AND SPRING ASSEMBLY — Proper installation of assembly is important. See appropriate chapter for procedures.

*DIAPHRAGM GASKET — Gasket and diaphragm sequence may be reversed on some models. Head of rivet must touch inlet needle. Rivet is hooked into inlet needle control lever on some models. See appropriate chapter.

*DIAPHRAGM

ATMOSPHERIC VENT HOLE — Hole must be clean on models with bulb primer vent hole is very small and is located off center.

IDLE SPEED ADJUSTMENT SCREW — Loosen screw until it just clears throttle lever, then turn screw in one turn.

THROTTLE SHAFT AND LEVER

DETENT REFERENCE MARK ON THROTTLE SHUTTER — Place detent reference mark to proper location. See chapter appropriate to specific carburetor.

THROTTLE SHUTTER

IDLE, INTERMEDIATE AND AIR BLEED ORIFICES — Remove welch plug and blow air through air passages.

*IDLE ADJUSTMENT SCREW AND "O" RING (If Present) — Remove adjustment screw.

*MAIN ADJUSTMENT SCREW AND "O" RING (If Present)

WELCH PLUG (If Present)

*MAIN NOZZLE CHECK BALL (If Present) — Check ball is not serviceable on some models. See appropriate chapter for specific model.

* NON METALLIC ITEMS – CAN BE DAMAGED BY HARSH CARBURETOR CLEANERS

FUEL AIR ☐ MIXTURE ▨

AUTOMAGIC TYPE

BEFORE START

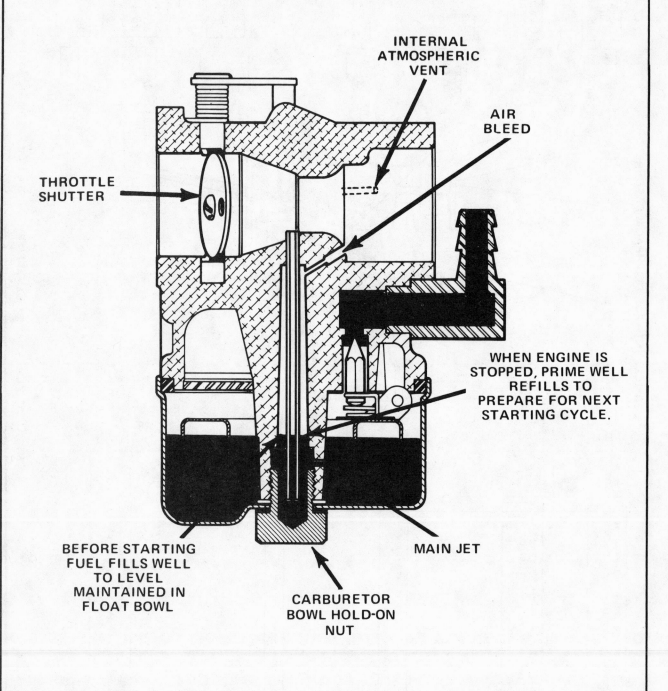

INTERNAL
ATMOSPHERIC
VENT

AIR
BLEED

THROTTLE
SHUTTER

WHEN ENGINE IS
STOPPED, PRIME WELL
REFILLS TO
PREPARE FOR NEXT
STARTING CYCLE.

BEFORE STARTING
FUEL FILLS WELL
TO LEVEL
MAINTAINED IN
FLOAT BOWL

MAIN JET

CARBURETOR
BOWL HOLD-ON
NUT

RUN

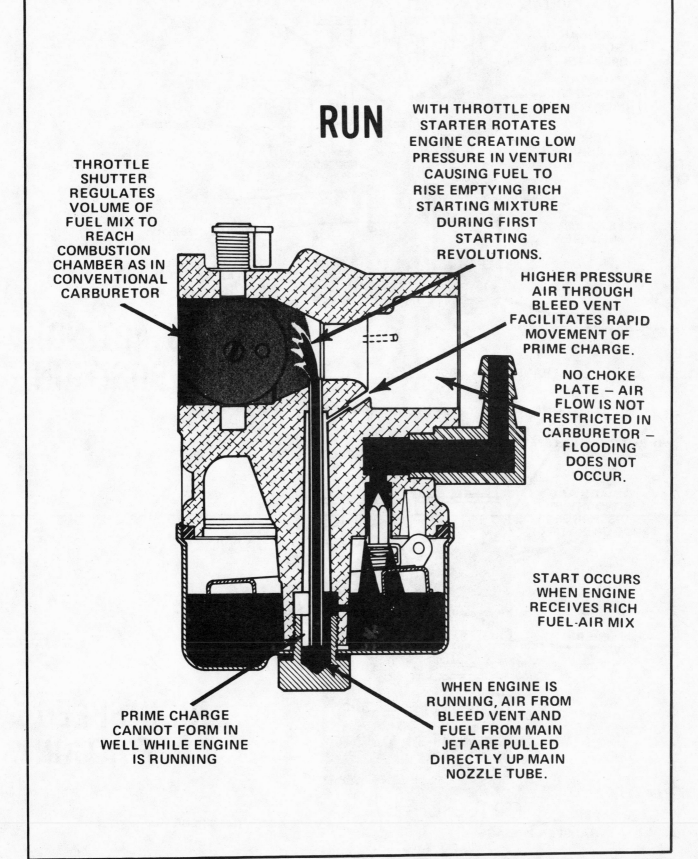

THROTTLE SHUTTER REGULATES VOLUME OF FUEL MIX TO REACH COMBUSTION CHAMBER AS IN CONVENTIONAL CARBURETOR

WITH THROTTLE OPEN STARTER ROTATES ENGINE CREATING LOW PRESSURE IN VENTURI CAUSING FUEL TO RISE EMPTYING RICH STARTING MIXTURE DURING FIRST STARTING REVOLUTIONS.

HIGHER PRESSURE AIR THROUGH BLEED VENT FACILITATES RAPID MOVEMENT OF PRIME CHARGE.

NO CHOKE PLATE — AIR FLOW IS NOT RESTRICTED IN CARBURETOR — FLOODING DOES NOT OCCUR.

START OCCURS WHEN ENGINE RECEIVES RICH FUEL-AIR MIX

PRIME CHARGE CANNOT FORM IN WELL WHILE ENGINE IS RUNNING

WHEN ENGINE IS RUNNING, AIR FROM BLEED VENT AND FUEL FROM MAIN JET ARE PULLED DIRECTLY UP MAIN NOZZLE TUBE.

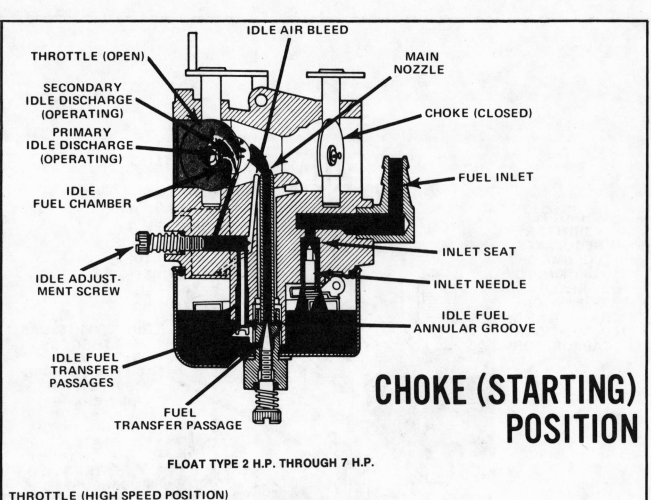

IDLE AIR BLEED

THROTTLE (OPEN)

SECONDARY
IDLE DISCHARGE
(OPERATING)

PRIMARY
IDLE DISCHARGE
(OPERATING)

IDLE
FUEL CHAMBER

IDLE ADJUST-
MENT SCREW

IDLE FUEL
TRANSFER
PASSAGES

FUEL
TRANSFER PASSAGE

MAIN
NOZZLE

CHOKE (CLOSED)

FUEL INLET

INLET SEAT

INLET NEEDLE

IDLE FUEL
ANNULAR GROOVE

CHOKE (STARTING) POSITION

FLOAT TYPE 2 H.P. THROUGH 7 H.P.

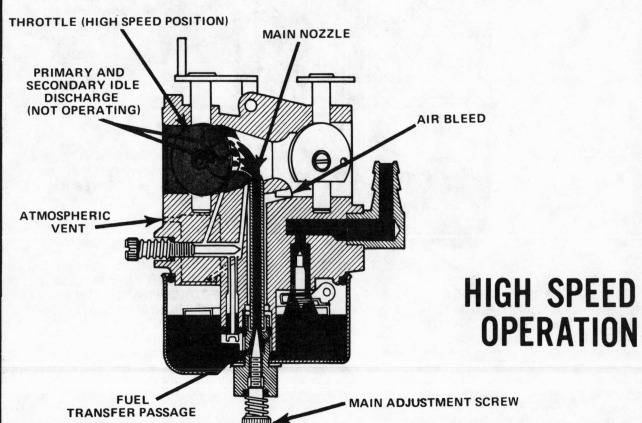

THROTTLE (HIGH SPEED POSITION)

MAIN NOZZLE

PRIMARY AND
SECONDARY IDLE
DISCHARGE
(NOT OPERATING)

AIR BLEED

ATMOSPHERIC
VENT

FUEL
TRANSFER PASSAGE

MAIN ADJUSTMENT SCREW

HIGH SPEED OPERATION

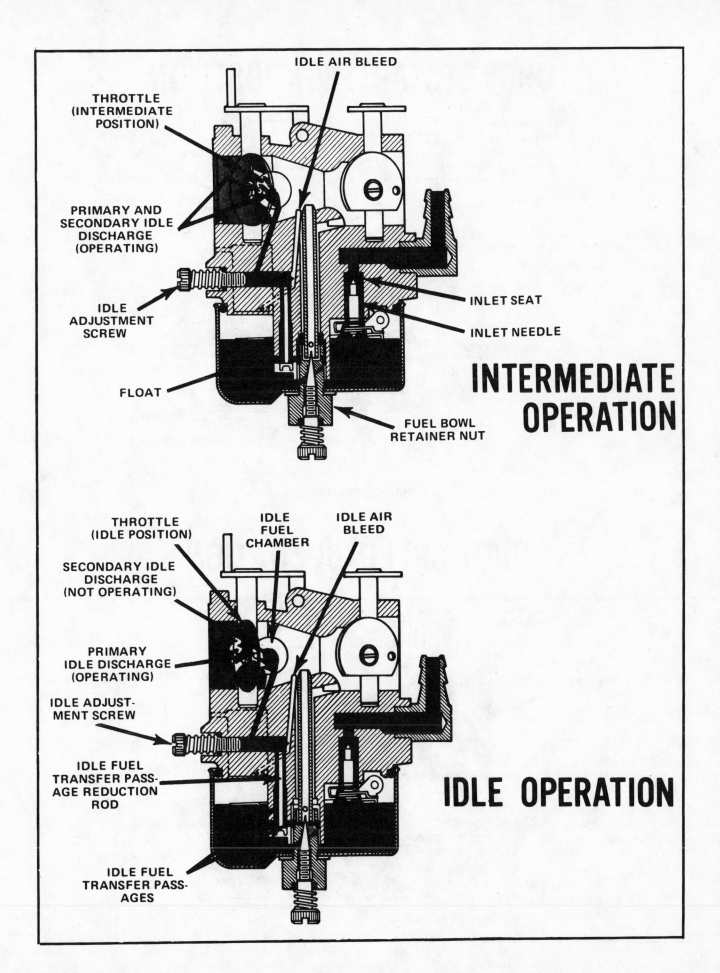

INTERMEDIATE OPERATION

THROTTLE (INTERMEDIATE POSITION)

IDLE AIR BLEED

PRIMARY AND SECONDARY IDLE DISCHARGE (OPERATING)

IDLE ADJUSTMENT SCREW

FLOAT

INLET SEAT

INLET NEEDLE

FUEL BOWL RETAINER NUT

IDLE OPERATION

THROTTLE (IDLE POSITION)

IDLE FUEL CHAMBER

IDLE AIR BLEED

SECONDARY IDLE DISCHARGE (NOT OPERATING)

PRIMARY IDLE DISCHARGE (OPERATING)

IDLE ADJUST-MENT SCREW

IDLE FUEL TRANSFER PASS-AGE REDUCTION ROD

IDLE FUEL TRANSFER PASS-AGES

CHOKE (STARTING) POSITION

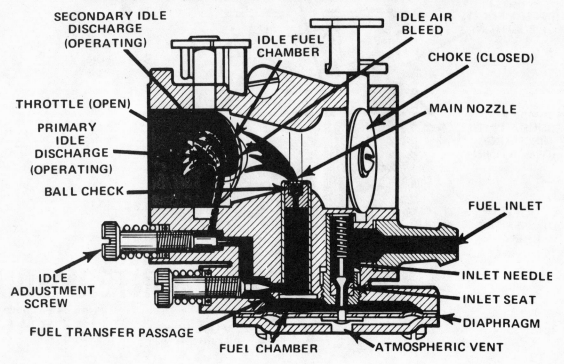

SECONDARY IDLE DISCHARGE (OPERATING)

IDLE FUEL CHAMBER

IDLE AIR BLEED

CHOKE (CLOSED)

THROTTLE (OPEN)

MAIN NOZZLE

PRIMARY IDLE DISCHARGE (OPERATING)

BALL CHECK

FUEL INLET

IDLE ADJUSTMENT SCREW

INLET NEEDLE

INLET SEAT

DIAPHRAGM

FUEL TRANSFER PASSAGE

FUEL CHAMBER

ATMOSPHERIC VENT

DIAPHRAGM TYPE

HIGH SPEED OPERATION

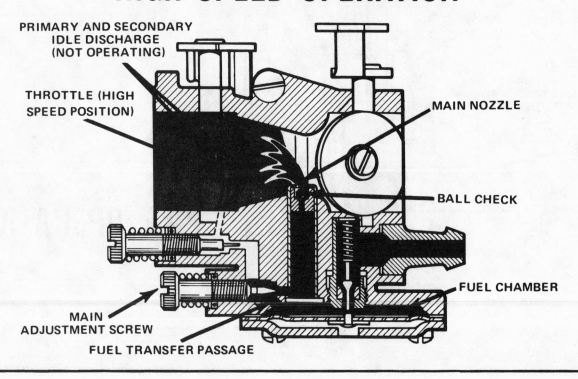

PRIMARY AND SECONDARY IDLE DISCHARGE (NOT OPERATING)

THROTTLE (HIGH SPEED POSITION)

MAIN NOZZLE

BALL CHECK

FUEL CHAMBER

MAIN ADJUSTMENT SCREW

FUEL TRANSFER PASSAGE

INTERMEDIATE OPERATION

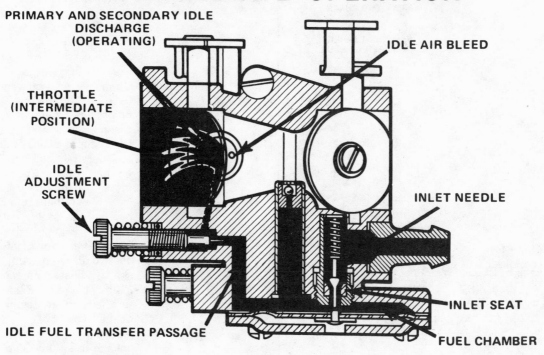

PRIMARY AND SECONDARY IDLE DISCHARGE (OPERATING)

IDLE AIR BLEED

THROTTLE (INTERMEDIATE POSITION)

IDLE ADJUSTMENT SCREW

INLET NEEDLE

INLET SEAT

IDLE FUEL TRANSFER PASSAGE

FUEL CHAMBER

IDLE OPERATION

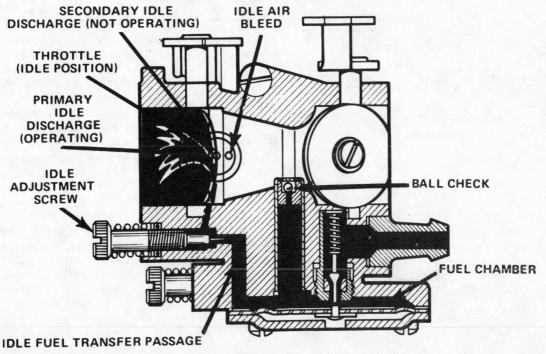

SECONDARY IDLE DISCHARGE (NOT OPERATING)

IDLE AIR BLEED

THROTTLE (IDLE POSITION)

PRIMARY IDLE DISCHARGE (OPERATING)

IDLE ADJUSTMENT SCREW

BALL CHECK

FUEL CHAMBER

IDLE FUEL TRANSFER PASSAGE

TROUBLESHOOTING

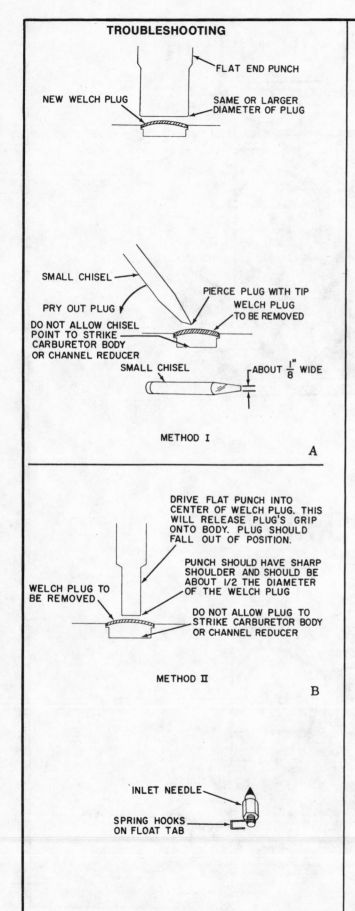

NEW WELCH PLUG

FLAT END PUNCH

SAME OR LARGER DIAMETER OF PLUG

SMALL CHISEL

PRY OUT PLUG

DO NOT ALLOW CHISEL POINT TO STRIKE CARBURETOR BODY OR CHANNEL REDUCER

PIERCE PLUG WITH TIP WELCH PLUG TO BE REMOVED

SMALL CHISEL

ABOUT 1/8" WIDE

METHOD I

A

DRIVE FLAT PUNCH INTO CENTER OF WELCH PLUG. THIS WILL RELEASE PLUG'S GRIP ONTO BODY. PLUG SHOULD FALL OUT OF POSITION.

PUNCH SHOULD HAVE SHARP SHOULDER AND SHOULD BE ABOUT 1/2 THE DIAMETER OF THE WELCH PLUG

WELCH PLUG TO BE REMOVED

DO NOT ALLOW PLUG TO STRIKE CARBURETOR BODY OR CHANNEL REDUCER

METHOD II

B

INLET NEEDLE

SPRING HOOKS ON FLOAT TAB

TROUBLE	CORRECTIONS
Carburetor out of adjustment.	Clean air cleaner; adjust main mixture adjustment screw. Adjust idle mixture adjustment screw. Adjust idle speed screw. Adjust control cable or linkage to assure full choke and carburetor control. Adjust governor linkage.
Engine will not start.	Open fuel shut-off valve at fuel tank — fill up with gas. Check ignition, spark plug, compression. Clean air cleaner. Dirt or restriction in fuel system; so clean tank and fuel strainers, check for kinks or sharp bends. Check for stale fuel or water in fuel; replace with fresh gas. Check fuel line and pick-up for sealing at fittings. Tighten. Examine throttle and choke shafts for binding or excessive play — free up or replace shaft. Adjust main mixture adjustment screw. Adjust idle mixture adjustment screw. Check position of choke and throttle plates. Adjust control cable or linkage to assure full choke and carburetor control. Check fuel pump operation — pump element, inner and outer one-way valves. Check diaphragm for cracks or distortion and check nylon check-ball for function.
Engine will not accelerate.	Check ignition, spark plug, compression. Clean air cleaner. Adjust main mixture screw. Adjust idle mixture screw.
Engine speeds up, slows down, "hunts."	Clean air cleaner. Clean tank and fuel strainers. Examine throttle and choke shafts for binding or excessive play. Remove dirt, replace shaft. Check throttle and choke return springs. Check idle and main mixture screws. Adjust screws. Adjust governor linkage. Adjust float setting. Check gasket and diaphragm — are they installed correctly? Check spring tension on governor.
Engine will not idle.	Clean tank and fuel strainers. Check throttle and choke shafts for binding or play. Clean, or replace shaft. Examine throttle and choke return springs for operation. Adjust main mixture, idle mixture and idle speed screws. Adjust governor linkage, adjust float setting. Check diaphragm for cracks or distortion. Check diaphragm and gasket. Check governor spring tension.

Engine lacks power at high speed.	Check ignition, spark plug and compression. Clean air cleaner. Examine fuel line for sealing at fittings. Examine throttle and choke shafts for binding or excessive play. Remove dirt; replace shaft. Adjust main mixture, and idle mixture screws. Adjust governor linkage. Diaphragm cracked needs replacing. Nylon check ball needs replacing. Diaphragm and gasket faulty.
Carburetor floods.	Dirt in fuel system; clean tank and fuel strainers. Clean atmospheric vent holes. Inlet needle and seat need replacing. Adjust float setting. Check float shaft for wear and float for leaks and dents. Check diaphragm for cracks or distortion and nylon check ball for function.
Carburetor leaks.	Check fuel line fittings. Clean atmospheric vent holes. Check idle and main mixture screws, and "O" rings for cracks and damages. Check sealing at welch plugs, cups, plugs and gaskets. Check seal for fuel drain or bowl gasket.
Engine over-speeds.	Check throttle and choke shafts for binding or excessive play. Replace shaft. Check throttle and choke return springs. Adjust main mixture screw. Check position of choke and throttle plates. Adjust control cable or linkage to assure full choke and carburetor control. Check seating of welch plugs, cups, plugs and gaskets. Adjust governor linkage.
Idle speed excessive.	Examine throttle and choke shafts for binding or excessive play. Remove dirt. Replace shaft. Examine throttle and choke return springs for operation. Adjust idle speed screw. Check position of choke and throttle plates. Adjust control cable or linkage to assure full choke and carburetor control. Check sealing of welch plugs, cups, plugs and gaskets. Adjust governor linkage. Check diaphragm for cracks or distortion; check nylon check ball for function. Check sequence of gasket and diaphragm. Check spring tension on idle governor.
Choke does not open fully.	Check throttle and choke shafts for binding or excessive play. Remove dirt, replace shaft. Examine throttle and choke return

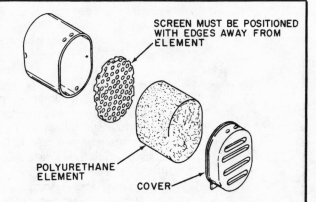

SCREEN MUST BE POSITIONED WITH EDGES AWAY FROM ELEMENT

POLYURETHANE ELEMENT

COVER

Polyurethane Air Cleaner

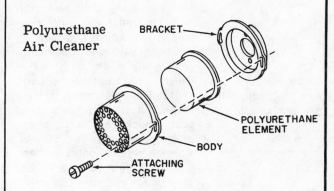

BRACKET

POLYURETHANE ELEMENT

BODY

ATTACHING SCREW

Paper Air Cleaners

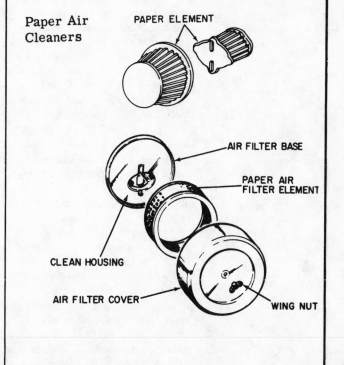

PAPER ELEMENT

AIR FILTER BASE

PAPER AIR FILTER ELEMENT

CLEAN HOUSING

AIR FILTER COVER

WING NUT

	springs for proper operation. Adjust control cable or linkage to assure full choke and carburetor control.
Engine starves for fuel at high speed.	Open fuel shut-off valve at fuel tank; fill tank. Check ignition, spark plug and compression. Clean air cleaner. Dirt or restriction in fuel system; clean tank and fuel strainers, check for kinks or sharp bends. Examine fuel line fittings for sealing leaks. Adjust main mixture screw. Adjust control cable or linkage to assure full choke and carburetor control. Check inlet needle and seat for condition and/or proper installation. Check fuel pump operation — pump, inner and outer one-way valves. Adjust float setting. Check gasket and diaphragm seating, leaks, etc.
Carburetor runs rich with main adjustment needle shut off.	Check and clean atmospheric vent holes. Adjust main mixture screw. Check inlet needle and seat. Check sealing of welch plugs, cups, plugs and gaskets. Check fuel pump operation. Adjust float setting. Check diaphragm for cracks or distortion and check nylon check ball for function. Check sequence of gasket and diaphragm.
	Open fuel shut-off valve at fuel tank. Fill tank with fuel. Check ignition, spark plug and compression. Clean air cleaner. Dirt or restriction in fuel system — clean tank and fuel system — clean tank and fuel strainers, check for kinks or sharp bends. Check for stale fuel or water in fuel. Fill with fresh fuel. Examine fuel line and pick-up for sealing at fittings. Check and clean atmospheric vent holes. Examine throttle and choke shafts for binding or excessive play — remove all dirt or paint, replace shaft. Examine throttle and choke return springs for operation. Examine idle and main mixture adjustment screws and "O" rings for cracks or damage. Adjust main mixture adjustment screw — some models require finger tight adjustment. Check to make sure it is correct screw. Adjust control cable or linkage to assure full choke and carburetor control. Clean carburetor after removing all non-

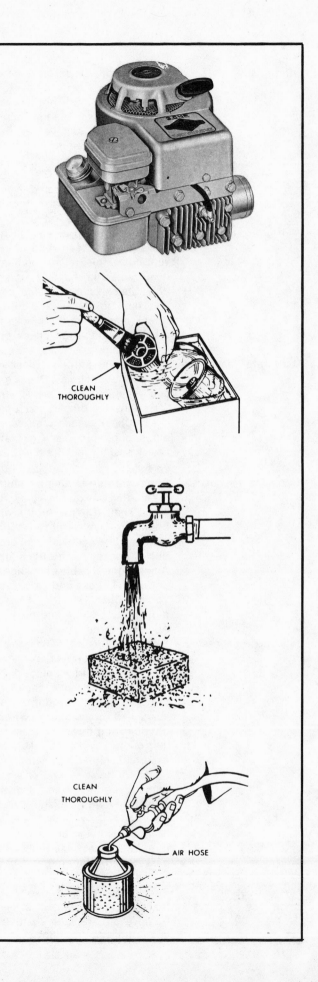

CLEAN THOROUGHLY

CLEAN THOROUGHLY

AIR HOSE

Performance unsatisfactory after service.	metallic parts that are serviceable. Trace all passages. Check inlet needle and seat. Check sealing of welch plugs, cups, plugs and gaskets. Adjust governor linkage. Adjust float setting. Check diaphragm for cracks or distortion and check nylon check ball for function. Check sequence of gasket and diaphragm.

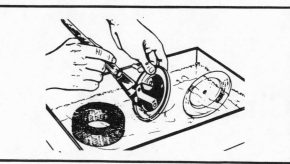

Lawn mower storage

If your lawn mower has no function in winter you should take several steps before putting it into hibernation. First, run the engine until the gas is used up. If the tank is full you'll have to get the gas out excepting for a small amount at the bottom. You can siphon it out with a rag — slosh the rag in it, then squeeze out the rag into a container. Some mower engines have valves that drain the tank (not many). Others have couplings you can loosen and drain (messily). Once the gas is drained completely — the engine has sputtered to a halt — you want to drain the oil and change it. (If you have a 2-cycle this step isn't necessary.) Clean off the underside of the mower, once you've drained out the oil. Clear away all grass, and other

debris with a wire brush or scraper of some sort. If rust is there, clean that off and paint it with anti-rust paint.

Next, remove the spark plug and put a spoonful of motor oil into the spark plug hole, and use the starter on the motor a few times, to move the piston and valves around a bit, distributing the oil thereby. Replace the spark plug. While you're at it, you might clean out the carburetor air filter, if you haven't done it lately.

When re-starting the mower engine for the new season it's a good idea to check out the muffler. These screw-in, cylindrical parts wear out slowly and imperceptibly. They rust into the coupling and may require a lot of penetrating oil to get them out. You can find them sticking out somewhere near the carburetor. Look for something that spews out smoke (and much air pollution); that should make it easy enough to find.

Chapter Four

Tillers and Snow Throwers

Two powered tools making the suburban scene are snowblowers and small tillers. With their 2 to 4-h.p. Briggs & Stratton, Clinton or Tecumseh engines, these very similar devices obviously do very different things. Churning snow out of the path, as against churning up the path to plant vegetables, are drastically different. With do-it-yourself gardening now all the rage, the small, fairly inexpensive tiller is zooming in sales. It pays for itself in time and energy saved, and it enlarges the scope of the garden. It can also be shared by several families (so too, snowblowers).

Let's look first at the socially more useful tiller. We will be talking about a typical, quality brand, the Ariens, which uses Briggs & Stratton and Tecumseh engines. Ariens is a useful, prototypical point of departure for the discussion.

The Ariens Jet Rotary Tiller comes in five different models, going up in power from the Model 320S, 3-h.p., to 624SR, 6-h.p. In between are the 420S, 424SR (both 4-h.p.), and the 524 SR.

Ariens also makes bigger, more powerful tillers.

Engine trouble-shooting is identical with earlier descriptions. The accessory systems (that is, all systems other than the engine) involve the forward and reverse clutch, belt and pulleys, handlebar adjustments, the speed change of tines (tines are what do the digging), the jet gear case, and on chain drive models, the chain case. All these systems have various adjustments and repairs, though few of them breakdown in actual use.

Belt and belt finger adjustments are important for maximum engine efficiency and clutch performance. Belt fingers are the curving rods in front of forward and reverse belt positions that control the belt movements at the forward and reverse idler wheels. These belt fingers must be positioned so as to clear the belt by very little — about 1/16-inch on the side of the belt that drives the pulleys — in the Ariens Rocket model, Jet Rotary models have the same clearance, with a clearance of 1/8-inch on the idler side of pulleys. To adjust belt fingers requires the loosening of cap screws holding fingers to the engine, with respective clutches engaged. Then set fingers to measurements (above) and tighten cap screws.

Clutch adjustment on the Jet Rotary Tiller is accomplished by moving the idler pulley so that no belt slipping occurs with clutch engaged, and when you disengage the clutch the belt de-clutches. So, move the idler pulley in the pulley bracket left or right until the precise tension is achieved that keeps the belt taut and without slipping when the clutch is engaged.

On the Rocket model the clutch adjustment is on the spring. With engine stopped, engage clutch. Then loosen locking nut that fastens spring to idler pulley arm — that right-angled brace that juts out from the forward idler. Turn adjusting nut on pulley until the spring is compressed to 1-inch length. Then tighten the locking nut. On the reverse idler you engage the clutch in the reverse position. Loosen the locking nut and turn adjusting nut until the reverse idler exerts tension on the reverse belt. Tighten locking nut.

Drive belt adjustments on the Rocket model should only be undertaken after the clutch spring and reverse idler adjustments are checked. If belt is loose, unscrew the four cap screws that attach the transmission to the frame. Some of the cap screws are well hidden. Turn adjusting screws until the drive belts are tight, then tighten the four mounting screws. Now you have to readjust the clutch spring and reverse idler, as before.

On the Jet Rotary models one complaint is belts

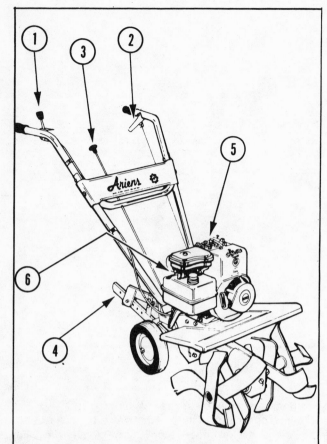

The Ariens Jet Rotary Tiller has six controls and adjustments beginning with (1) the throttle that controls operating speed. (2) is forward clutch control; (3) is reverse clutch; (4) adjusts depth of tilling; (5) engages to stop engine; disengages to start and (6) is choke for starting. Forward and reverse clutches are adjusted by moving the idler pulley to left or right in the slot of the pulley bracket. Belt fingers are adjusted while clutches are engaged. Handlebars adjust on swing and stationary models. Standard handlebar adjustment is effected by loosening nuts that hold handlebars to frame, then moving them to desired position. Tighten upper bolts first. Swing handlebars adjust by loosening cap screws and nuts holding braces to main post.

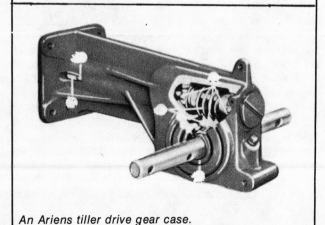

An Ariens tiller drive gear case.

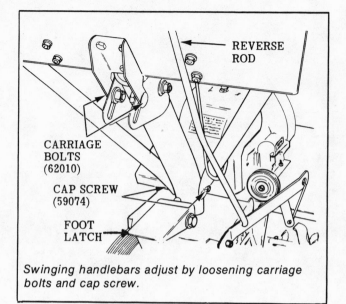

Swinging handlebars adjust by loosening carriage bolts and cap screw.

that are too tight and won't respond to adjustment. One cause, oddly enough, is wrong size belt. On Model 72099 the size is 31-inches. Model 72056 takes a 32-inch belt; 72043 gets 32-inch belt also. Some belt complaints, however, are more serious and stem from a bent frame. If pulleys are out of alignment with each other that's a guarantee that the frame is bent and has to be replaced.

Handlebar adjustments are simply to make the operator comfortable with the height. Handlebars bolt to the frame, and you need merely loosen the bolts and pull or push the handlebars into the most comfortable height

Belts clear belt fingers by very small margins.

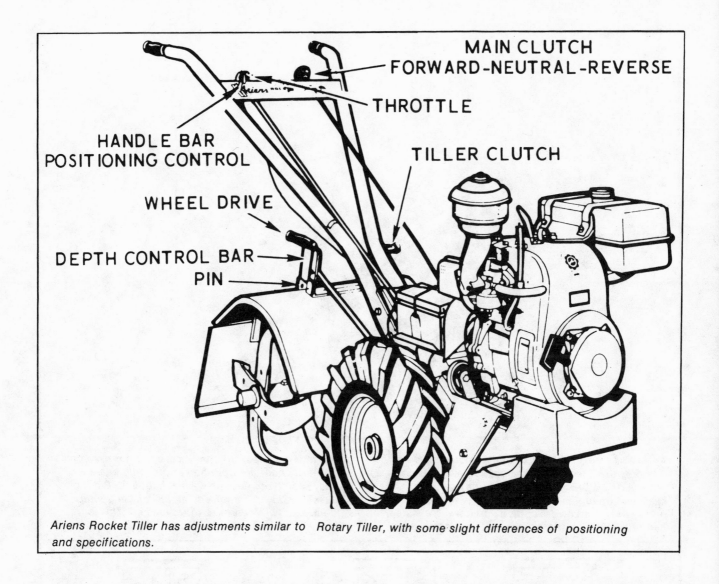

MAIN CLUTCH
FORWARD-NEUTRAL-REVERSE

THROTTLE

TILLER CLUTCH

HANDLE BAR
POSITIONING CONTROL

WHEEL DRIVE

DEPTH CONTROL BAR
PIN

Ariens Rocket Tiller has adjustments similar to Rotary Tiller, with some slight differences of positioning and specifications.

for the most frequent operator. Swing handlebars are a little more complex but not much. To be loosened are the nuts at the bottom of the braces where they join the main post, and at the handlebar panel.

To change the tine speed of the Swing Handlebar tillers from tilling to cultivating speed, or vice versa, requires shifting the belt on the drive pulleys. Front position is slow; rear is fast (from 75 rpm to 100 rpm). Disconnect spark plug cable. Remove belt guard, then pull the belt partly off the lower sheave in the direction it turns. Pull on the starter rope and move the belt. Start the belt on the top sheave, and pull the starter rope and move the belt. Start the belt on the top sheave, and pull the starter rope to roll belt fully on the sheave. Install the belt guard and connect the spark plug.

Transmissions to drive the tines on these machines are somewhat simplified auto transmissions, hence involve complications of design and repair. When they develop oil leaks you can pull the seals out and replace them without tearing down the whole box. Other transmission repairs, however, are complex and involve major surgery with tools like an arbor press, bearing driver

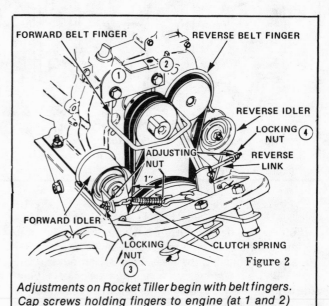

FORWARD BELT FINGER   REVERSE BELT FINGER

REVERSE IDLER

LOCKING
NUT ④

ADJUSTING
NUT

REVERSE
LINK

1"

FORWARD IDLER

LOCKING
NUT
③

CLUTCH SPRING

Figure 2

Adjustments on Rocket Tiller begin with belt fingers. Cap screws holding fingers to engine (at 1 and 2) control this adjustment. Reverse and forward idlers adjust after loosening nuts at 3 and 4.

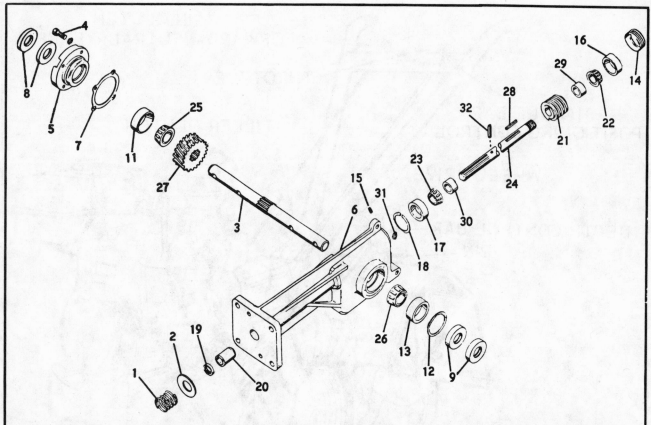

An Ariens transmission like this one obviously has complexities for any home mechanic with visions of repairing a burned out bearing or gear. Oil seals can be replaced as at (8) and (9) with a bit of prying from a screwdriver or, if you have it, a slide hammer. But, after that the difficulties arise because bearings and bearing cones have to be pressed in and out. There are both ball and needle bearings, also. Each type requires special handling. But if oil seals leak, at (19), at (9), and at (8), you can replace them. You will then have to replace oil. This is a special transmission gear lube.

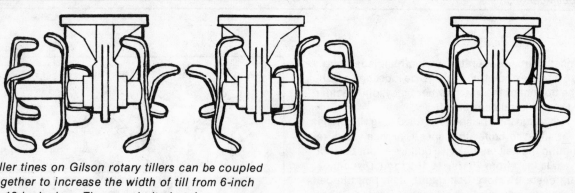

Tiller tines on Gilson rotary tillers can be coupled together to increase the width of till from 6-inch to 18-inch sizes. Tines are bolted on in a prescribed order.

and others that do not warrant buying unless you plan to go into the business. To replace oil seals, however, requires only removing the tines, then prying out the end seals with a screwdriver, and banging new ones in. Each side of the tine drive shaft has two sets of oil seals that pry out. The easiest way to get them out is with a slide hammer. It hooks the inner surface and pulls the seal out.

The wheel drive transmission on the self-propelled machines, riding machines and tractors, involves greater complications than the home mechanic should undertake to repair. The tiller drive clutch, however, can be repaired easily enough if something happens to it, but it is virtually foolproof. The transmission is a device of a different order — an automobile type transmission with dozens of moving parts.

On the Gilson rotary tiller, Model 51095, belt ad-

TROUBLE SHOOTING CHART FOR ARIENS JET TILLER

JET

MODEL	TYPE OF FAILURE	CAUSE	SOLUTION	SERVICE BULLETIN
All models except chain drive	Gear Case Failure (Run Tight)	UNKNOWN (suspect lack of, or improper oil)	Replace damaged parts and use Ariens L-2 Oil in Gear Case	
	Oil Leaking from Gear Case	Seal Failure	Replace (2) 56049 seals with (1) 56066 double seal.	SB-4-70
	Oil Leaking from Gear Case	Lack of Sealant on lower Flange Bolts	Use Sealant on lower bolts	
All 1974	Tight Belts Tight Belts	1) Short Belts 2) Bent Frame 3) Miswelded Frame 4) Idler touching belt in out position. 5) Too many shims under engine.	1) NEW BELTS. Belt lengths 72099 - 31'' 72056 - 32'' 72043 - 32'' 2) Check pulley alignment to determine frame trueness 3) Center distance of pulleys should be 9-5/32''. If not replace frame. 4) Adjust idler. 5) Remove a shim.	
	End play in 2003 worm shaft	Worn 2005 spacer	Replace 2005 spacer and check snap ring	

justment is not needed. When replacing belt (because it is worn, cracked, frayed or burned) it is essential to order by part number. To replace, remove the belt guard. Then slip the belt over the top of the engine pulley until it comes off — if it will. If it won't, loosen the engine bolts and tilt the engine in to the belt. Then it will certainly come off. Don't remove the engine bolts. When putting on the new belt, fit it around the bottom pulley assembly first, and then around the top of the engine pulley. If you loosened the engine bolts you must re-tighten them. Replace the belt guard, making certain that the tab on the guard is pushed against the side of the engine. Never run the tiller without the belt guard.

Gilson's Model 51095 is interesting because it is very compact and portable. It weighs 51 pounds and has a 2-h.p. engine, a Briggs & Stratton. This engine differs from other Briggs engines we've discussed only in that it has a manual choke instead of an automatic. (Tillers mostly have manual chokes.) The gear case on this tiller is permanently lubricated. If grease leaks develop at the seals of the gearbox, they can be easily replaced by removing the tine assembly and pulling out the seals. But there are two felt seals and a seal collar assembly that guard against leaks, effectively.

Handle adjustments on the Gilson Model 51095 can be made when the wing nuts on the sides of the handle are loosened. The handle can then be adjusted to the most comfortable length. Before re-tightening, make certain that the washer face of the wing nut is seated precisely in the enlarged adjustment opening of the handle.

Other service on this model tiller consists of lub-

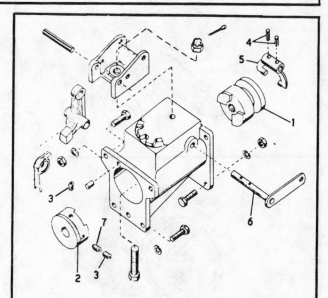

The tiller drive clutch for the Ariens Rocket Tiller has a neat simplicity to it that will not baffle you if you try to repair it. A cotter pin secures the clutch operating rod to the clutch lever. When this is disconnected you can remove cap screws and hex nuts that bolt the clutch to the transmission housing. Then the clutch comes apart fairly easily, beginning with clutch jaw (2), which is held in place by two Allen set screws (3). Other components are bolted in. They include, chiefly, the splined clutch jaw (1), and the clutch yoke (5).

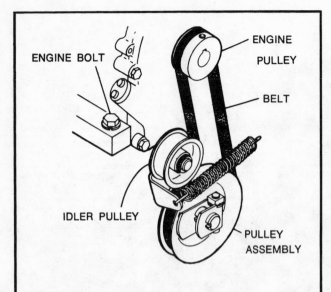

ENGINE BOLT

ENGINE PULLEY

BELT

IDLER PULLEY

PULLEY ASSEMBLY

ricating the wheels, and the idler pulley shaft (the engine, of course, but that is covered in earlier sections). To lubricate the wheels, take them off — they unbolt easily. Clean them and oil all moving and touching surfaces with 30 weight engine oil. The idler pulley shaft should be given the same kind of oil, but avoid spilling any on the belt. When oiling, turn the pulley around. Adjustment of tilling width is accomplished by the interchanging of tines, or the removing of one or both of the outer tine hub assemblies. Tilling widths vary from 6-inches up to 18. Tines are bolted on with a cap screw and washers. It is vital that the lock washer always be used, and that it be placed against the cap screw. The order is the cap screw (the bolt), lock washer, flat washer, and the square tine washers. Tines, by the way, go on in only one direction.

PUSH "TAB" DOWN AGAINST THIS SURFACE

"TAB"

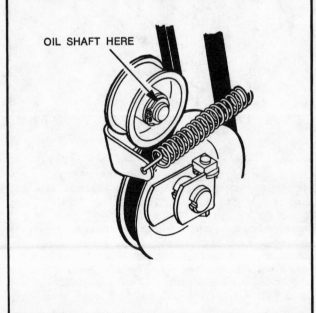

OIL SHAFT HERE

Gilson tiller (right) has tine locking mechanism illustrated in exploded view. Below, an Ariens tiller showing major components including transmission to drive tines.

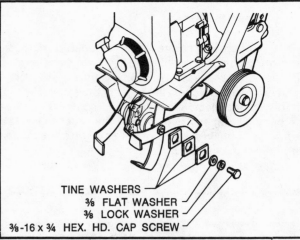

TINE WASHERS
⅜ FLAT WASHER
⅜ LOCK WASHER
⅜-16 x ¾ HEX. HD. CAP SCREW

Snow throwers

Suburban type snow removal tools are, perhaps, far more common than tillers. They have small engine, clutches and transmission or gearbox, and the belt system to drive wheels or auger (the auger is the snow tiller that churns up and ejects the snow from the blower tube or discharge chute). In Ariens models the usual engine is a Tecumseh, but Briggs & Stratton engines are common throughout the industry.

The whirling auger is geared down to turn slowly and powerfully, to chew up the snow and feed it to the impeller, which is a high-speed blade that throws the snow out to distances of up to 25 feet. The snow blower requires heavy tires (snow tires), and the auger housing is forward system that does all the work, and like the tine system on tillers, is subject to much bumping around, and possible damage from obstructions. It is wise to keep it away from too-rugged terrain.

Some snow throwers have brushes that sweep up the snow, but these are much less common than the throwers. Not all snow throwers work in the two-stage operation described above — auger to impeller. In some

An International snow thrower model with adjustable snow blower chute.

An auger on a snow thrower.

over-loading the engine, which is a four to six horsepower that easily invites over-loading. You don't want to run the engine at maximum speed, which over-loads it; but so does running it at too slow a speed. Generally, the best speed is about an idle speed or slightly above. If the engine resists working at this speed it needs tuneup. Heavy snow will, however, require full speed ahead.

The slow-speed auger, with its slicing, forcing thrust, and the high-speed impeller — which is a combination slicing and pumping device — combine into the most efficient way to move snow quickly and easily. Controls to manage this combination should be forward and reverse, with several forward speeds available. A clutch to cut out the auger and the forward motion of the thrower is essential, and the best design is the sort that requires pressure from the operator's hand to activate and the release of the hand to stop it. Some machines have over-load protection that stops the auger when it picks up something buried in the snow and starts it through the process. You don't want your snow thrower hurling rocks, sticks and stones — which can break bones. Ariens uses a shear pin design that causes the pin to shear off. It is quickly and easily replaced. It is also desirable that the clutch distinguish between the wheels and the auger — that it can stop the auger without, however, stopping the wheels. This is a convenience for moving the thrower without worrying about getting the auger into something other than snow.

The Gilson snow thrower has a throttle, a choke, traction clutch shift lever, and an impeller clutch. The auger and impeller work in tandem and are controlled

throwers the auger and thrower stages are combined into a single stage. Such machines are called single-stage (in a burst of blessed simplicity of nomenclature). Snow throwers take some skill from the operator, as well as from the mechanic who would maintain them. The operator must know how to manipulate through many different kinds of snow — powdery, wet, and all stages in between. Wet snow tends to plug up the chute and the way to avoid this is to establish a brisk pace of operation. Sufficient volume of snow forced into the chute will force snow out of it, usually. But this also introduces the possibility of

simultaneously. Needless to say, control of the direction of snow throw is also essential, and all throwers have such a control. This changes direction to suit the direction of the wind, and keeps the snow out of your face.

A pattern of snow throwing is important to use, otherwise you may wind up throwing snow from one undesired area into another. The best pattern is to go up the center and return in an arc, as follows:

SNOW REMOVED TO EITHER SIDE

START

FINISH

SNOW REMOVED TO EITHER SIDE

NO SNOW PILED ON LEFT SIDE
START ON LEFT SIDE

ROTATE CHUTE 180°

SNOW REMOVED TO RIGHT SIDE ONLY

Gilson and some other models have automobile type grease fittings that require regular grease gun attention at the opposite ends of the auger, and though without grease jets the snow chute and idlers usually require lubrication with grease.

Belt adjustment on Gilson throwers is not required, since belts are spring-loaded and operate under tension. Belt track on the pulleys should be checked from time to time. Belts sometimes remove themselves due to pulleys coming loose, or the idler becoming out of line. The idler should meet the belts precisely on center. When drive is engaged, the belt fingers need to be within 1/16-inch to 1/8th-inch of belts.

To replace belts on the Gilson requires removal of the belt guard and belt guide, the impeller idler spring, and the auger belt from the engine pulley. Next, force the belt down and off from the bottom groove of the auger pulley. It should now be resting on the auger housing. Next, remove the auger bearing from both ends of the

shaft. The entire auger and impeller assembly can now come out. The old belt will come out; replace it with the new one. Before you slide the auger-impeller assembly back, have the new belt resting on the bottom of the auger housing.

The traction drive belt is pretty much the same to remove, excepting that after you remove the auger bearing from the two ends of the auger shaft you then remove the traction drive idler spring. Then the old belt comes off, the new one goes on.

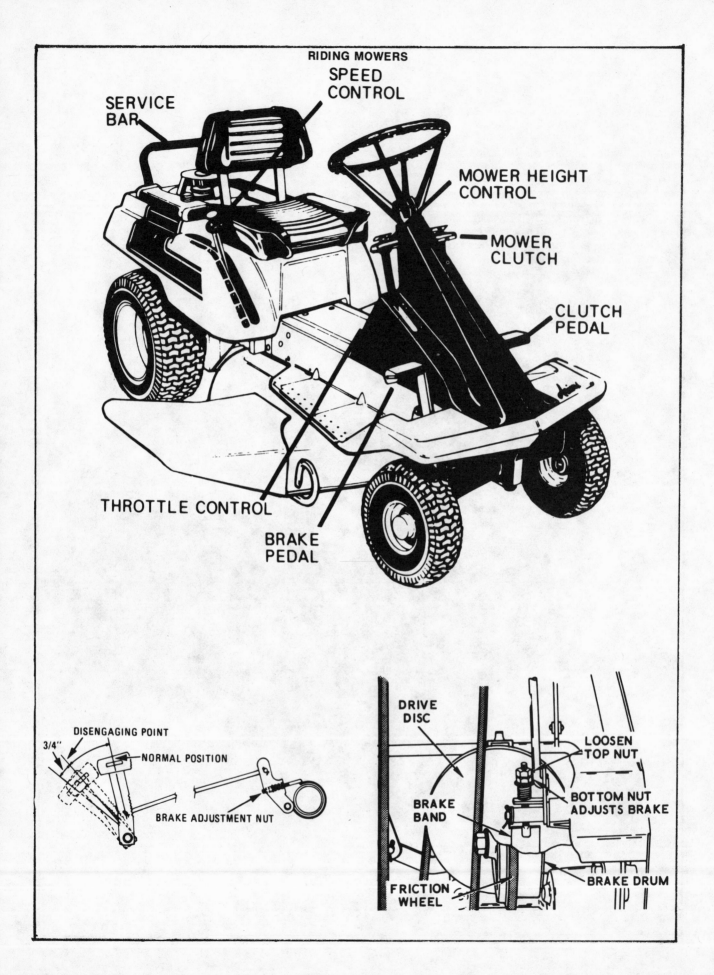

RIDING MOWERS

SPEED CONTROL

SERVICE BAR

MOWER HEIGHT CONTROL

MOWER CLUTCH

CLUTCH PEDAL

THROTTLE CONTROL

BRAKE PEDAL

DISENGAGING POINT

3/4"

NORMAL POSITION

BRAKE ADJUSTMENT NUT

DRIVE DISC

LOOSEN TOP NUT

BRAKE BAND

BOTTOM NUT ADJUSTS BRAKE

FRICTION WHEEL

BRAKE DRUM

An Ariens riding mower showing controls, service bar and major components. Service bar is used on most adjustments, and requires that it be bolted into place. Adjustments, in addition to engine service (exactly similar to earlier discussions), include clutch, brake, steering, belts, and wheels. Brake adjustment is shown on previous page. Loosen lock nut. Push clutch pedal until friction wheel disengages. Hold clutch pedal ¾-inch past disengaging point, rotating both rear wheels. Brake should drag slightly. Tighten lock nut. If brake doesn't drag at this point, adjust bottom nut until it does. In addition to the wheel brake adjustment, there is also the mower brake adjustment (at right). It requires that the brake chain anchor be adjusted until it has a slight sag.

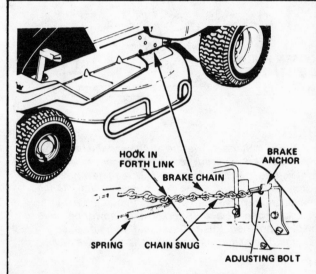

The mower brake adjustment on the Ariens riding mower, as noted on the left, requires loosening the brake chain by means of the adjusting bolt until the chain sags slightly. You can check adjustment: engage mower clutch and see whether brake releases as belt begins to tighten. The chain should be loose when height adjustment lever is in HIGH and LOW positions.

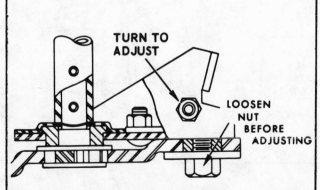

Steering adjustment is needed when there is excessive play. Loosen nut then turn to adjust, as illustrated, until play is reduced.

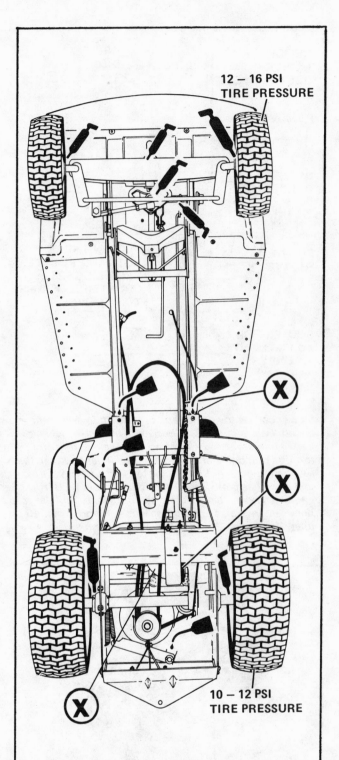

The Ariens Emperor 3000 Series riding mower requires special lubrication at points marked X; oil is required at those places indicated by oil cans; grease guns point to those places requiring regular greasing. Tires need inflation as noted. The Ariens manual prescribes intervals for lubrication and greasing.

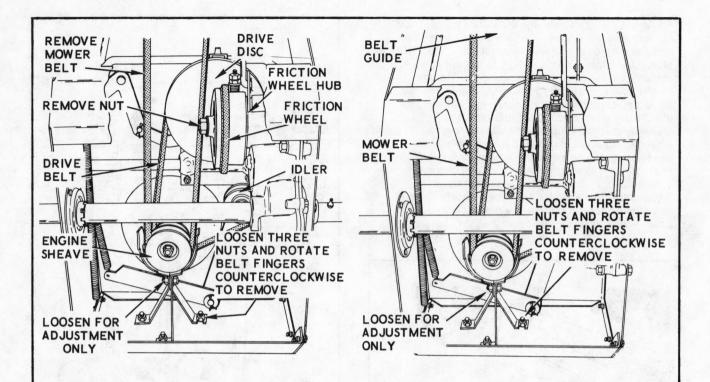

REMOVE MOWER BELT

DRIVE DISC

FRICTION WHEEL HUB

REMOVE NUT

FRICTION WHEEL

DRIVE BELT

IDLER

ENGINE SHEAVE

LOOSEN THREE NUTS AND ROTATE BELT FINGERS COUNTERCLOCKWISE TO REMOVE

LOOSEN FOR ADJUSTMENT ONLY

BELT GUIDE

MOWER BELT

LOOSEN THREE NUTS AND ROTATE BELT FINGERS COUNTERCLOCKWISE TO REMOVE

LOOSEN FOR ADJUSTMENT ONLY

Mower belt removal and replacement on Ariens riding mowers requires that the mower be on the service bar. Mower clutch lever is in the OUT position. Three nuts holding belt finger should be released; rotate belt finger until free. Roll belt off mower sheave. Remove swivel pin at rear and "U" bracket will be free. Belt comes off. Thread new belt through belt guide around rear pan hanger and then to mower sheave. Replace "U" bracket and swivel pin. Replace rear belt fingers, tightening the top two nuts first. Drive belt removal and replacement goes like this: remove battery and drain gas tank. Speed control lever is in NEUTRAL. Remove engine sheave belt fingers; rotate mower belt free of engine sheave. Release drive belt from idler. Shift lever to sixth speed position. Push clutch shaft to gain space between drive disc and friction wheel. Remove belt. Replace belt and thread it around engine sheave, drive disc and idler. Now replace mower belt and rear fingers.

DEPRESS SPRING CLIP WITH WRENCH AND TURN FOR BELT ADJUSTMENT. REPOSITION CLIP.

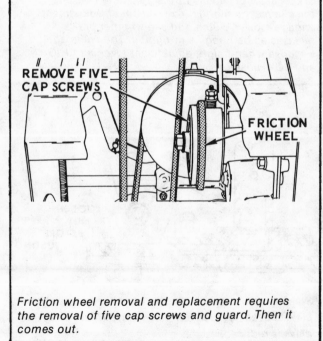

REMOVE FIVE CAP SCREWS

FRICTION WHEEL

Friction wheel removal and replacement requires the removal of five cap screws and guard. Then it comes out.

Chapter Five

Power Saws and Hand Tools

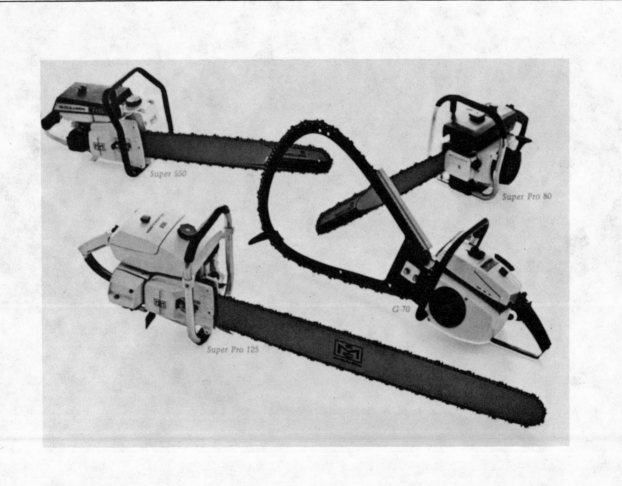

Chain saws

There are two kinds of chain saw power sources — electric motor and gasoline engine. The gas engine is a small, two-cycle engine exactly like a small lawn-mower engine with one main difference, the avant-garde carburetor that will work in any position.

Trouble shooting in a gas engine power saw, when it fails to start or run smoothly and responsively to the accelerator, is exactly as it is in the engines we've been talking about. Ignition and fuel systems, the valves, piston, connecting rod, bearings, flywheel, magneto, muffler, and accessory parts, work as they do in the larger, 4-cycle engines, excepting that the engine has two less cycles.

One component in the saw not present in the mower is the centrifugal clutch, which powers the chain. The clutch operates only when the engine speeds up above idle speed. The principle of a centrifugal clutch is familiar to boys with coaster brakes for inside the brake is such a device. Friction pads are forced out against the drum, as in an automobile hydraulic brake, to engage and turn the sprocket wheel that in turn spins the chain.

Actually, the centrifugal clutch has two parts — first, the driving section consisting of the end of the engine's crankshaft around which a three-spoked device called a "spider" turns. The three spokes turn the movable shoes, which are held by springs. When engine speed accelerates the shoes are forced out, centrifugally, against the drum which turns a sprocket wheel, like the sprocket on a bicycle. This in turn, forces the chain to move around its guide bar.

The chain itself, which looks somewhat like a bicycle chain but isn't, has three kinds of links: (1) drive links that hook into the sprocket and hold the chain on the guide bar; (2) cutting links designed to cut from both left and right; and (3) side links that hold drive and cutting links together and permit the chain to flex around the guide bar and sprocket.

The chain is oiled continuously by a button that can be pushed during operation and allows oil from the chain's private oil tank to drip onto the chain.

The chain needs occasional sharpening and adjusting of tension, and replacement of damaged links. A chain that has lost its tension wears out links fairly rapidly. Tension is easily adjusted and adjustment is necessary when the chain is loose enough to be readily pulled around the bar by hand — it should be taut and resist pulling. The chain bar adjusting nut should be loosened with a wrench; next with the chain bar in horizontal position turn the tension adjusting screw until the chain resists being pulled. Now tighten the adjusting nut with the wrench and check tension to make sure it didn't change during the tightening of the nut. If it did, repeat the process and allow for the tightening of the nut in calculating the correct tension.

If the chain needs sharpening you need a file guide and a round file, which you should buy at the time you purchase the saw. Instructions will explain that with the file guide you can sharpen the chain easily enough if you have the patience to file away carefully and correctly.

The file guide has marks on it to indicate the correct angle of file — the guide marks should parellel the chain. You position the file in the guide and file blades on one side of the chain. File from inside of each cutting tooth, then to the outside. Maintain the guide in correct position — flat on the cutting blade. File each blade on one side of the chain, sharpening them all at the same point on the chain bar, and file them the same amount — count the strokes. Then do the same thing with the blade teeth on the other side of the chain. You can buy an

expensive sharpener, by the way, with a small electric motor and three sharpening stones. But we recommend the clamp-on sharpener we've been talking about.

To repair chains you can also buy a special tool. It locks into the chain, punches out the rivet, enabling you to put in an adjustable anvil and a new rivet. The tool installs the new rivet. In the Sears catalog this tool is called "Break-N-Mend" and sells for around $15, but you can buy a similar tool at any well-stocked hardware or at the shop where you bought the saw.

When the chain has to be replaced, remove the bar adjusting nut and loosen the tension adjustment screw. Then remove the cover over the clutch. Now the chain will come off the sprocket and then from the chain bar. Put the new chain on exactly as the old one fit, then adjust tension as before.

Engine maintenance begins with the usual tuneup procedures, excepting that the carburetor is entirely different, and one additional maintenance is required, the cleaning of carbon from the exhaust ports. This has to be done periodically or whenever the engine seems to be below par and you can't find any other reason. It is well to begin there, in fact, since it is more accessible than the usual systems that cause engine weakness. You want to remove the muffler cover, next to the spark plug cable, or nearby, then uncover the exhaust ports by removing the clip that is held by a couple of screws. Once the exhaust port clip or shield is off you can clean everything off. First, clean off the muffler cover, then the exhaust port shield. Now, turn the engine over until the

piston completely covers the exahust ports — if it isn't in that position. This prevents carbon from falling into the cylinder — a no no. Scrape off the carbon from the ports with something soft — don't use a knife unless you use a very dull one and don't use that unless you do it gently. The preferred tool is a carbon scraper with fingers that yield and don't claw into metal surfaces. You can buy one for very little.

Regular engine maintenance should always begin with the ignition system. First, remove the spark plug cable, then remove the spark plug. Procedures and specs will be exactly similar to earlier ones in this book.

Once the spark plug is cleaned and gapped, or replaced — depending on how it looks and how long it has been in operation, and a rule of thumb is that the spark plug should be replaced every season when the engine is used fairly often — you need to investigate points and condenser. If points need replacing soon after they've been replaced it means the condenser is faulty. If points look okay — they show no wear — but the engine exhibits point failure symptoms — it is probably the fault of the condenser. On Tecumseh 2-cycle engines, which you may encounter in a gasoline engine trimmer, the flywheel removal is slightly different than with Briggs & Stratton or Clinton engines. In addition to using a knock-off technique, or a wheel puller device, you may find it necessary to use a butane torch. If you find that the knock-off method doesn't work at all, or if the flywheel puller strains without doing the job, use a butane torch on the area just outside of the crankshaft. The aluminum alloy of the flywheel

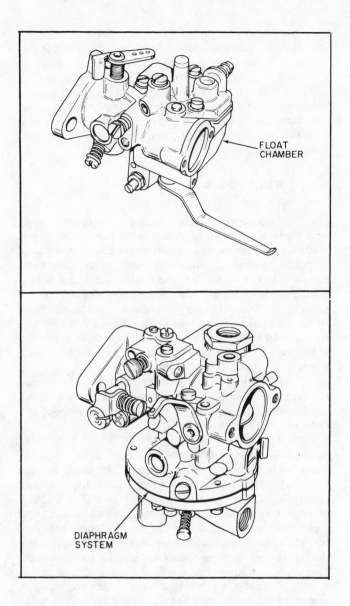

FLOAT
CHAMBER

DIAPHRAGM
SYSTEM

testing a magneto requires the use of special equipment. You'll have to rely on the shop for such service. At least you'll know it isn't the spark plug, points or condenser. And magnetos rarely conk out; electrical troubles are almost certainly in the spark plug, points and condenser.

As noted, the carburetor on the chain saw engine is different from the lawn mower and other small engine applications; it has to work at any angle. Such carburetors are called pressure differential. They have a diaphragm exposed to crankcase pressure on one side and atmospheric pressure on the other — like the Briggs Pulsa-Jet. As crankcase pressure decreases the diaphragm moves against an inlet needle, which moves away from its seat. This opens the gate for gas to flow through the inlet valve in order to maintain correct fuel level in the fuel chamber. To adjust carburetors on Tecumseh chain saw engines first remove the needle valve (one of three screw adjustors) to check it for ridges or other wear. The screw tip should be perfectly tapered and without wear. Rub your fingernail over it; if you feel anything you need a new one (that is, if you feel any worn ridge on the tapered tip of the valve). Now screw in the valve until it seats gently — any force will ruin it and/or its seat. This valve and the main adjustment screw below it both should be turned back out 1 complete turn. At the top of the carburetor is the idle screw which regulates idle speed by pushing on the throttle. For preliminary adjustment, back it out, then turn it back in until it makes contact with the throttle lever. Then turn it one more complete turn. Now warm up the engine thoroughly — cut down a small branch or two (no Redwood trees). Allow the engine to idle by opening the choke and releasing the throttle. If the engine now dies, turn the idle speed screw in until the engine idles okay but does not turn the chain. Now adjust for smoothness of engine performance — of course, if the engine works smoothly now, let it alone. If it does not, next turn the idle mixture needle (just above the main screw or air adjustment screw) just a bit to the right or left — whichever has a smoothing effect on the idle. You seek maximum speed without moving the chain. If the chain turns now, turn the idle speed screw back. Squeeze the throttle quickly. If the engine fails to accelerate, or hesitates, turn the main screw a bit counter-clockwise. That should do it, unless the carburetor needs rebuilding. In any case, fairly frequent carburetor adjustment is required on chain saws because of the rough treatment. Not all carburetors have three screw adjustors; some have a fixed main and idle mixture screw.

If adjustment fails to produce a correct idle, the next step is a peek into the bowels of the carburetor. Dirt is the usual cause of carburetor breakdown, but wear on moving parts — especially the diaphragm and the inlet needle — is normal and a cause of poor performance.

In tearing down a Tecumseh chain saw carburetor avoid soaking non-metallic parts in carburetor cleaner. These parts include ''O'' rings, a nylon check ball, the inlet needle and seat, the diaphragm and diaphragm gasket. Of course, most of these parts are candidates for replacement, since they involve critical areas of wear. But, often the only thing wrong with carburetors is accumulated dirt. Once that is removed, the thing may work like

will expand under the torch to break the seal from the crankshaft, which is steel. Normally, the knock-off tactic will work, and the flywheel puller will work when the knock-off won't. So Butane is the court of last resort for recalcitrant flywheels.

On the 2-cycle Tecumseh engines, once the flywheel is out, look carefully at the points. First of all, check the gap, which should be .015. If it's larger or smaller any engine malfunction could be caused by the incorrect gap. If the points are burned, corroded or worn off, replace them and the condenser. On Tecumseh engines remove the nuts over the electrical leads on the moveable point spring, then remove the moveable point from its stud — a somewhat similar system to the Briggs engine design. Then remove the screw and the stationary point. Install the new stationary point on the plate; finger tighten the screw. Put the new movable point on its post. Now adjust the point gap against the peak point of the cam, and tighten the screw. The correct point gap will be shown on the dust cover. Tighten screws, and check again for correct gap.

If you are still not getting correct spark from the engine it means the magneto is not working correctly. But

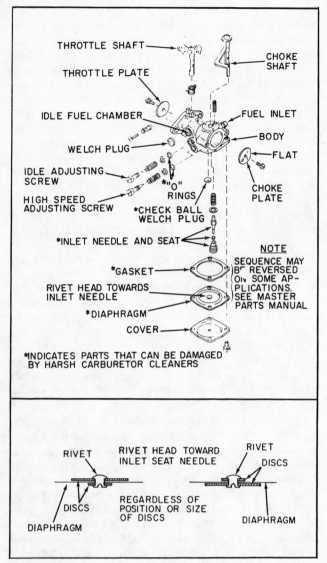

THROTTLE SHAFT
THROTTLE PLATE
IDLE FUEL CHAMBER
WELCH PLUG
IDLE ADJUSTING SCREW
HIGH SPEED ADJUSTING SCREW
*"O" RINGS
*CHECK BALL WELCH PLUG
*INLET NEEDLE AND SEAT
*GASKET
RIVET HEAD TOWARDS INLET NEEDLE
*DIAPHRAGM
COVER
CHOKE SHAFT
FUEL INLET
BODY
FLAT
CHOKE PLATE

NOTE
SEQUENCE MAY BE REVERSED ON SOME APPLICATIONS. SEE MASTER PARTS MANUAL

*INDICATES PARTS THAT CAN BE DAMAGED BY HARSH CARBURETOR CLEANERS

RIVET
RIVET HEAD TOWARD INLET SEAT NEEDLE
RIVET
DISCS
DISCS
REGARDLESS OF POSITION OR SIZE OF DISCS
DIAPHRAGM
DIAPHRAGM

new. A diaphragm must be replaced when it shows any sign of damage, wrinkling, pin holes, cracks and tears. It may be inspected by removing the four screws that retain the diaphragm cover to the carburetor body. When replacing the diaphragm the diaphragm rivet head goes toward the inlet needle valve. Also, replace the gasket, and make sure you replace these parts with identical new ones. The inlet needle valve and seat should also be replaced at the same time, unless the needle valve is perfectly smooth and without wear. To remove the inlet needle and seat requires a bit of doing. For one thing, some models need a screwdriver with a slot in the middle, to fit over the unit. Others come off with a socket wrench but with precious little space to maneuver in. When removing the inlet needle you must watch for a spring to pop out.

The typical Tecumseh carburetor on chain saws has a separate idle circuit that passes through the carburetor body and goes to the bottom of the engine crankcase. Air for the idle section is metered by an offset shutter that directs it through the air horn. Gas flows through a restrictor in the carburetor fuel passage line which meters out the gas. An intermediate circuit that controls normal engine operation connects to the idle circuit, but is fed through the air horn in the usual way. Separation of the idle system from the intermediate circuit is needed because of the nature of the usage that the chain saw gets — when idling, the saw usually is sitting upright, or is held upright; when the saw is being used the intermediate circuit is called into play. If engine idle cannot be adjusted satisfactorily it means dirt or other blockage, which only an examination can reveal, and a soaking of the carburetor in cleaning chemical can cure.

HAND TOOLS

Circular saws use an electric motor to spin a steel saw blade at high speed. Management and care of the blade is the most important maintenance, since the blade, if dulled, becomes ineffective and even potentially dangerous. For home use, the best circular saw is one with complete blade cover, with some type of "motor saver drive" that cushions the motor against blade shock when the blade hits nails or knots. Blades can be sharpened with tools designed for the job, or they can be sharpened professionally, but if the correct blade is used it will retain its cutting edge for a long time.

Motor maintenance on a circular saw is minimal. Bearings usually are sealed and many saws have accessible brushes that can be inspected visually without the need of elaborate tearing down.

The sabre saw or jig saw is the most popular home saw. It cuts wood, metals and plastics when the appropriate blade is used with a saw possessing the correct capability. Better sabre saws have fairly complex components, in addition to the usual motor. Dialed speed settings, electronic sensors that maintain constant speed and torque, anti-vibration mechanism, air-blast chip ejector, and other sophisticated settings and controls, make the sabre saw a complicated as well as versatile tool. There are, of course, much simpler designs.

Typically, a sabre saw has a motor anchored in sealed ball bearings with a fan at one bearing. The motor drives a helical gear set that turns an eccentric cam that is linked to the plunger which is attached to the blade below. The plunger is lubricated by felt seals at each end which either must be lubricated by hand from outside, or which have lubrication built in. A switch to select the speed — high, medium, low — and a tilting base and blade support complete the components. Good sabre saws will have some kind of balancing mechanism internally that minimizes vibration. Anything driving itself at high speed up and down automatically manufactures vibration. One test of the quality of the sabre saw is the level of its vibration.

To maintain a sabre saw in the style to which you need it isn't different from any hand power tool, unless you have one of the models with sensors and other complications. The basic components, however, require the same greasing and cleaning, attention to the motor and its brushes, that any hand power tool requires. The plunger must be kept in oil; its seals will need replacing sooner or later. When the seals wear out, oil gets out and dust gets in. This can lead to trouble in the gears and motor. So, a

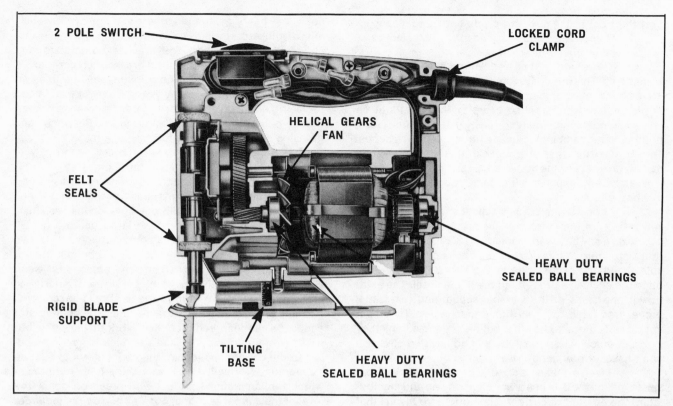

2 POLE SWITCH

LOCKED CORD CLAMP

HELICAL GEARS
FAN

FELT SEALS

HEAVY DUTY SEALED BALL BEARINGS

RIGID BLADE SUPPORT

TILTING BASE

HEAVY DUTY SEALED BALL BEARINGS

periodic inspection, change of seals and lubrication will prolong the maximum efficiency of the sabre saw. The seals, plunger and blade attachment bolt into the front plate support that is part of the case. Four bolts usually need removing to get at the front components.

A comparatively new power saw called a "recipro" (for reciprocating) or all-purpose saw, cuts virtually anything — metal pipe, steel, wood with embedded nails, regular cuts of wood. It's a kind of sabre saw, excepting that it is more versatile and more powerful. Usually with a trigger speed control that offers low, medium and high speed, the saw is compact and easily manipulated. It weighs usually under 10 pounds, and can make do with a comparatively small motor — 1/3d to 1/5th h.p., for example.

The reciprocating saw is, in effect, an elongated sabre saw, with a more or less identical driving mechanism, only it is laid out differently. The saw comes straight out instead of straight down. It is as if you were to take a sabre saw and stand it on its front end. It is maintained and repaired like the sabre saw, only the plunger is at the bottom instead of at the front. The versatility of the saw has allowed designers to give it many varied configurations, and to create various patterns of gearing as well. But the configuration that seems most adaptable to most jobs is the one we've been talking about — grip and switch at the rear, the motor standing on its end, and the gears, cam and plunger at the bottom with a foot swivel to sup-

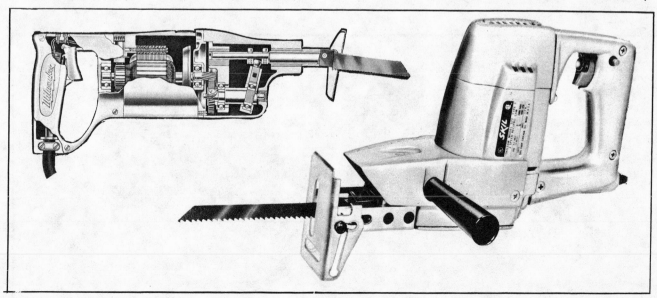

port the front of the saw and a side handle to steady it.

Maintenance and repair on the reciprocating saw is identical to the jig or sabre saw.

The commonest of all powered hand tools is the ¼-inch drill. This infinitely resourceful tool has done more for the home mechanic or do-it-yourself-er than any other single device. No task is so complex that it cannot be helped along or completely solved by this ubiquitous tool; nothing in higher mechanics is entirely outside its scope. The ¼-inch drill, like the 5-cent cigar, is what everybody needs, only unlike the vanished cigar, the drill is everywhere, and so inexpensive that some people collect them, like bottle tops.

A good ¼-inch drill is almost a fool-proof tool. If you take even the most rudimentary care of it, you will never have any back talk from it. The 3/8-inch and ½-inch drill also figure in this discussion. These drills, with variable speed and reverse, are taking over a lot of territory once the exclusive property of the ¼-inch drill. The extra power and skills of the variable speed, and reversible, prove irresistible to many home mechanics. They cost appreciably more, to be sure, but most people think they are cost efficient. Besides, there is no law that says you can't have several hand drills.

Reverse means an extra gear or two. Variable speed means the drill has a way of modifying and manipulating the amount of current. The larger size means that the drill can handle tougher jobs.

Maintenance on hand drills consists of greasing periodically, and replacing brushes. If the drill gets a lot of service, the switch can wear out, and so can the cord. So, indeed, can the gears and bearings. Hand drills, though not fragile, are subject to the laws of wear and decay. If a little tinkering can repair virtually anything, their low cost sometimes makes it un-economic to repair them. Still, some people become attached to a good hand drill, and prefer to keep it alive. To such people, the following remarks will make more sense than to those without sentiment about hand drills.

The parts of a drill consist of the case, the switch and cord, the motor with its commutator and brushes, coils, and bearings, the fan, gears and chuck. Obviously any of these parts can wear out, especially those that move. All the gears, bearings, brushes, commutator and the switch can wear out. Gears, if greased regularly, and if they are sturdy instead of the fragile types one finds on occasion, will wear for many years. Brushes won't need replacing often, unless the drill is used a great deal. Even then, a pair of brushes can last for years. Bearings need greasing as often as gears, for the same reason — heavy friction. If the typical sleeve bearing is greased every year or two it should last forever. So too the gears.

To grease gears and bearings requires taking apart the case. This means unscrewing the various through bolts and nuts, and breaking open the case in its two halves. Clean the gears with kerosine, and grease them generously with bearing grease. Grease the two sleeve bearings lightly and check the commutator for wear, arcing (carbon traces), and the brushes for wear. Brushes that show heavy wear, by virtue of shortened length and distorted wearing surface, should be replaced. Replace brush springs at the same time. The commutator should be sandpapered off until it is bright and shiny (but never with emery cloth). Then the mica laminations between the copper sections of the commutator should be "undercut." Normally this is a machine tool operation in which the laminations are cut with precision below the level of the copper sections. But if all you do is sandpaper lightly it isn't necessary to undercut the mica sections. Just take a fingernail file, or any thin, but sharp device, and scrape out all the fine grounds of copper that have fallen from the sandpaper. Blow it out carefully — if you don't have a powered source of air your lungs will go far toward doing the job. The mica is an insulator and so long as it doesn't interfere with the brushes in any way it will not need undercutting.

With the case apart, clean out all collections of dirt and grease. Check out the switch and the cord. Clean the fan. When replacing the case make certain that grooves match perfectly before tightening the through bolts or screws. Don't tighten excessively. Also, tighten in an opposed sequence, rather than in a circular pattern. It

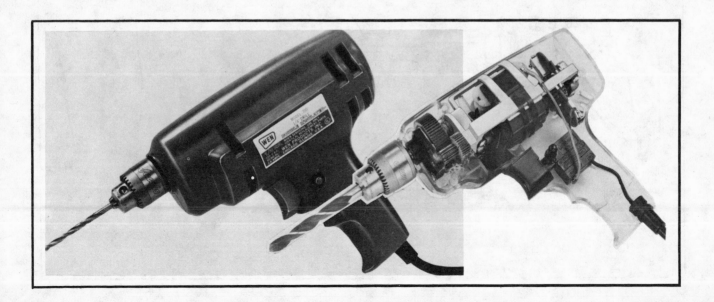

is a good idea to tighten very lightly, then plug in the tool and turn it on. If there is any sign of binding, either because of a new noise or a slower performance or starting ability, it means you haven't put the case and/or components back correctly.

All the above applies to a drill that you have no reason to believe is defective — you are merely doing routine maintenance on it. Trouble-shooting a drill is another matter. A drill that doesn't work, works lamely or noisily, gives off sparks or shocks, obviously needs more than routine maintenance. If the drill is inexpensive it is time for a new one. But if it is a prized, expensive tool, it can be repaired, normally at a far lower cost than replacement. If the rotor or stator is shorted or burned out (rotor: revolving element; stator, stationary), it may be impossible to repair the tool. But if it is a well-known brand the chances are that all parts can be replaced without difficulty. A new rotor or stator might turn out to be prohibitively expensive, but it is worth pricing. Any electric motor can be repaired; the only question is cost efficiency. If repairs exceed the cost of a new one obviously you shouldn't repair but replace. On the other hand, if you simply prefer the old tool to a new one you may opt for repair. Begin with brushes, whenever a small motor misbehaves. Also, check out the condition of bearings and gears. Wear in any of these components will cause binding and sharp interference with normal performance. If brushes arc and spark it is a sign of defective brushes or a short circuit in the commutator or in the rotor windings. Unless you have test equipment you'll have to take it to a shop where it can be assessed, for very little cost. (Many shops do this at no cost, in order to sell you a new one.) Once you establish the condition of the rotor, stator, bearings and gears, the brushes and their springs, and replace what is defective, you should have a tool that is more or less in perfect condition. The cord and switch should, as a matter of course, be looked at periodically, but when a switch fails it gives warning and you can see cord failure, usually. Switch failure is signalled by a switch that is hard to use or refuses to turn on correctly, or needs "jiggling" to make it work, or suddenly won't work at all — that is, when you turn it on nothing happens. This kind of total collapse of a tool that had been working can be the cord or a combination of cord, plug (electrical current source), and perhaps the switch, or one of the three. But you can always separate cord and switch symptoms from motor symptoms. If you can get the tool turned on by jiggling the switch or cord and it runs normally you can be sure it isn't the motor.

The hand drill and its attachments are basic to most home repair tasks, including many lawn mower and automobile repairs, for that matter. Most other tools with electric motors as the power source are variants of the hand drill. The powered hammer, the orbital and disc sander, the electric screwdriver, and even the jig saw, are hand drill motors with extensions that perform the specialized job that gives them their name. An orbital sander is a drill-type motor with an irregular cam that drives that sanding disc back and forth at a high speed. The only maintenance it requires is similar to drill maintenance — greasing of gears and bearings, as well as atten-

tion to the brushes and their springs. And, like the drill, it doesn't require that very often. A disc sander is a drill with a disc at right angle to the motor. One difference between hand drills and other small tools is that roller or ball bearings may be encountered, especially in more expensive, better quality tools. (Expensive and/or quality hand drills also have them.) Ball or roller bearings last longer and perform more rugged duties than sleeve bearings, but they do need occasional grease.

Other tools have other characteristics. A bench grinder is a motor fitted with two sanding discs. A belt sander is a more complex tool. It has an electric motor at the top, a timing belt drive, a revolving platen, special sanding belts (various sizes, usually three or four inches wide, and 20 to 24 inches), and two rollers around which the belt is turned.

Maintenance on a belt sander is usually confined to the belt itself and its rollers. The belts need regular replacement and replacement is easy enough, but any moving component in a tool is subject to wear and tear. Belt sanders wear at the belt itself, which is a gear tooth drive belt driven by a geared cam off the motor. Belt replacement is quick and easy, once you remove the cover. Service on the motor is simplified in some models by easily reached brushes (for example, on Stanley) and brush springs. Most bearings on these motors are permanently oiled or greased and need no attention in the normal course of events.

Power screwdrivers are hand drills fitted with

special clutches that hold the bit that drives the screw. Clutches are of several types, depending on the nature of the job. The positive clutch is used in materials of a non-uniform density — fastening wood, wood to metal, fiberglass to metal, for example. The adjustable clutch is used in soft materials. The depth adjusting clutch is for those jobs that require a precise depth control of the screw. A threaded, adjustable nose piece screws in or out to the required screw depth. The nose piece, as it surfaces on the material, disengages the driving clutch and the bit stops turning the screw. Care and maintenance of these tools is exactly similar to the hand drill. Other than cleaning, the clutches need no maintenance.

Trimmers

Hedge trimmers have a small electric motor, a gear to drive the movable blade, a fixed blade, and a fan to cool the motor. The two blades, 20-inches or so, can stand a little oil, occasionally. Sometimes the gear that drives the movable blade becomes worn and sometimes the blades wear out. Motor failure isn't common, but anything that moves can fail, especially if it is called upon for duty above and beyond the call (the rating). The gear turns an off-center disc that pushes the blade out and pulls it back. Wear sufficient to disable the trimmer can occur at this point, and a too-great burden on the blade can bend and

ruin it at the point of contact. Replacement of both malfunctioning parts is easy. In each case you remove the housing screws that hold the (usually) plastic case together and once this is done you can take out the blades and the gear and replace both of them. Re-grease everything that moves, (lack of grease is what caused the gear and disc to wear in the first place).

The electric cable and switch are the source of problems with the hedge trimmer. The cable can wear out and so can the switch. Switches are usually more feeble than cables and to replace the switch requires taking the case apart to get at it.

Motor maintenance in these devices normally isn't required. But the usual things can go wrong — brushes, bearings, and even burnouts if the motor is placed under too much pressure from cutting chores constantly beyond its capacity. Thin twigs and hedges are about its speed; it won't cut branches much over a quarter of an inch. Greasing and brush replacement require taking the case apart and removing the motor. Put bearing grease on the gears and all moving parts, and check out the condition of the commutator. If it is black use a piece of sandpaper on it, (never emery cloth) then inspect the brushes. Also check the springs. If the brush springs have lost their tension they need replacing. Weak springs are a prime source of poor seating and subsequent arcing in the commutator.

Grass trimmers, unlike hedge, are powered by a battery motor, small, but sturdy enough in capacity to cut grass in clumps and along sidewalks or wherever the lawn mower can't reach. Batteries in these trimmers will run for quite a few minutes — up to 45 on a single charge. The motor drives a set of gears and an eccentric cam or disc that propels a movable blade against a fixed blade, exactly as with the hedge trimmer. Only the blade is moved from side to side, like a pair of scissors. Recharging the battery is about the only problem. But the blades need sharpening once a season if the device gets much use. There are special sharpeners that are used when the blades are mounted. You can also remove the blades and sharpen them with a plain file. Mount the blades in a vise, one at a time, of course. To remove the blades, unscrew the two blade mounting screws.

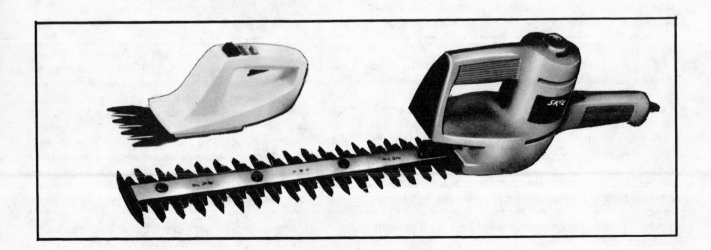